SURVIVAL AT NODULEX

SURVIVAL AT NODULEX

THE TIME-BASED ROUTE TO COMPETITIVE QUALITY

BY

PHILIP R. THOMAS

AND

KENNETH R. MARTIN

TCT®, 5 I's Process®, Cycles of Learning®, Total Cycle Time^SM, Resultant^SM, AIP Management^SM, AIPs^SM, Actions-In-Process^SM, and Opportunity Manager^SM are trademarks of Thomas Group, Inc.

ISBN: 1-879234-27-0

Library of Congress Catalog No. 94-079419

Printed and bound by Heritage Publishing, 9029 Directors Row
Dallas, Texas 75247.

First Printing

Manufactured in the United States of America

PREFACE

Here is a different kind of book about the role of quality in competitive business operations. Its purpose is to clarify the relationship between effective performance and high quality. To achieve that purpose, it debunks a few prevailing myths and outlines a system in which quality can be meaningfully defined and measured.

The pursuit of quality, a laudable objective, has distracted countless businesses from their underlying problems. Too often, troubled companies view quality improvement as a way to restore competitiveness and customer satisfaction. As this book will demonstrate, however, quality-improvement efforts do not improve competitiveness because quality by itself does not drive a business.

What drives a business, and in the bargain provides a meaningful index of both competitiveness and quality, is cycle time. A company with long cycle times and high quality standards is doomed. A company with short cycle times enjoys a working environment in which quality occurs naturally and customers are satisfied through timely, responsive service.

Survival at Nodulex is about time-based quality. Specifically, it details a system called Total Cycle Time, which any company can use to achieve world-class quality and world-class competitiveness. Total Cycle Time is derived from years of successful experience, not academic theorizing. It is a method that

- Creates a culture in which quality flourishes naturally

- improves responsiveness to customers, providing a quality of service that is meaningful and measurable to them

- eliminates distracting, parochial quality-improvement efforts within a company

- creates a system to exploit and apply the lessons of experience, which fosters continuous improvement

- establishes pertinent, accurate ways to measure quality

- succeeds in every type of business, including yours.

Total Cycle Time succeeds in every type of business because the underlying causes of uncompetitive performance and poor quality are generic. The barriers and challenges confronting Nodulex Corporation, described in this book, were no different from those obstructing effective performance in businesses everywhere. That is why the Nodulex story is worth reading.

Nodulex is a fictional company. The incidents and situations that constitute its story, however, are based upon countless real-world experiences, combined into a novelized format that provides a readable, coherent way to demonstrate the inseparability of time-based management and competitive quality.

The characters in the story are likewise fictional — all but one: Earl Gomersall. Gomersall was and is an original thinker in the field of performance improvement, one of the first to sense the relationship between short cycle time and quality. Gomersall has known Philip Thomas for thirty years, and for the last seven has been a *Resultant* at Thomas Group, Inc. The concepts he espouses in this fictional setting are, like the principles of Total Cycle Time, tested and proven in real-life situations.

If your business is manufacturing, service-based, labor-intensive, or high-tech, you can learn much about true quality — competitive quality — from *Survival at Nodulex*. You might even turn your own company around!

Chapter One

NO   LEX CORP

What's a nice girl like you doing in a place like this? she thought as she steered her minivan down I-95. Ann Moore was no stranger to this patch of unlovely industrial interstate southwest of Philadelphia, but until today it had seemed only a blur on the way to somewhere else. Not any more. If her final interview came off okay and she took the job at Nodulex, commuting to Essington would be part of the daily grind.

What a change! For six years, Moore had been chief financial officer at Philadelphia-based Brikabrak Technologies (Briktek). Lately, to her surprise, she was also the strongest of three candidates shortlisted for the vacant CEO slot at Nodulex Corporation. Moore's Briktek experience had boosted her candidacy because, for years, Briktek and Nodulex had shared a close and profitable association. The association had lately grown less close and less profitable by the month, a sure sign that Nodulex needed new managerial blood. But, Moore wondered, was her blood the right type?

During her first interview, Nodulex people had given Moore a tour of the company and a rundown of the "challenges" she would face if she became the next CEO. Rundown was also the right word to describe the physical plant, she thought. Definitely not love at first sight. But somehow, matters had gone forward, and today was her last interview — decision time.

Out of anxiety, and out of character, Moore had exceeded the speed limit, which put her in Essington ten minutes ahead of schedule. Because she made it a point always to arrive on the dot for appointments, she used the extra time for another look at her possible professional future, trying in vain to spot something encouraging. Or attractive. Or auspicious. Anything.

No such luck. Nodulex lay just off the Industrial Highway, a few hundred yards from the Delaware River. Nearby was the Philadelphia International Airport and the troubled Naval Shipyard. The surrounding landscape was dominated by oil refineries and storage tanks, but the river and surrounding flatlands mitigated the smokestack effect and allowed breathing space to a few blue-collar, red-brick neighborhoods like Essington. Today, with the wind blowing upriver from Marcus Hook and Chester, the reek of refining oil was downright distracting. How could people live here? Moore wondered. More to the point, how could people work here?

Moore tooled slowly up the long Nodulex driveway, noting how sunlight glinted off old fragments of glassy litter. Approaching the plant, she could see that aside from glass-cube trim around its main doorway, the sprawling, two-story, early-twentieth-century brick structure was devoid of architectural flourishes. It sat amidst several acres of asphalt surrounded by a cyclone fence, leased land that was once part of a U.S. Navy seaplane base but which now provided parking space for a wide variety of employee vehicles, old and new. Through cracks in the asphalt grew thriving clumps of sumac, the trash tree of choice among the region's rundown sites. Atop the plant's flat roof, a malfunctioning sign proclaimed NO   LEX CORP in twelve-foot neon letters. For several years, she knew, that broken sign had symbolized the dysfunctional character of its owners, and "NOLEX" became the local epithet for a company in decline. Looks can be deceiving, Moore thought as she rolled into the visitor parking area, but not this time. What you see is what you get.

Why then was she flirting with this company's board? Because the headhunter who had found her swore that the company could be turned around — provided someone like her took command.

Early in her candidacy, Moore had been briefed by Headhunter in his Center City office, a minimal, white-walled suite enhanced by framed vintage movie posters and a wide-angle view of the Ben Franklin Parkway. "What Nodulex needs," said Headhunter, stubbing out his umpteenth cigarette of the day, "is someone from outside who is committed to quality, sticks to the principles of time-based management, and won't flinch at the changes to be made. People like that are hard to come by. But your Briktek record shows me that you fill the bill." He paused to let that sink in, leaning in close with an ingratiating smile. Such a smoothie, thought Moore. Someone should tell him to quit breathing smoke on his clients. She, however, was not that someone.

What about expertise in Nodulex products? Moore had none. "Not a problem," soothed Headhunter in his confiding way. "In fact, it's an asset. The Nodulex board admits that the company got into a rut of its own making. They've concluded that outside talent is a must and, for once, they're right. But — and I can say this for sure because I've looked — they're not going to raid the competition for expertise. Can't. Potential candidates working for competitors are convinced that Nodulex's days are numbered. Needless to say, they won't touch this company with a ten-foot pole. Why should they buy a ticket on the *Titanic*?"

Scant encouragement to Moore. "Why should I buy a ticket on the *Titanic*?"

"Because," said Headhunter, "One man's, or rather one person's, *Titanic* is another person's Starship *Enterprise*. All is not lost at Nodulex. Look: The Nodulex board is scared witless. They know the company is screwed up but they don't have a clue about how to put things right. As you know, the company is closely held, and they've been talking to themselves too long. Most board members belong to the Lotz family, with a couple of lawyers and friendly outsiders thrown in. Over the last decade, the board and senior management became overcomplacent. By the time they woke up, industry standards were changing. The company's product quality and performance deteriorated sharply compared to the competition.

"Since the wakeup call, Nodulex has been frantically grasping at straws. They've tried remedy after remedy to no avail. They've thrown money in all directions. They've run themselves ragged. But they're still losing market share. You're from Briktek, Ann, so this story should sound familiar."

It was indeed familiar. Briktek had undergone a similar fall from grace but caught itself in the nick of time. As Briktek's CFO, Moore had participated in a dramatic quality and performance turnaround. The approach, known as Total Cycle Time, involved a ruthless examination of every cycle of activity within Briktek and the elimination of any step in any cycle that added no value to the task. The struggle was painful and difficult but, throughout the company, processes had been simplified and shortened with astounding results.

As distractions and red tape were stripped away, Briktek's ability to effectively serve customers had skyrocketed. It became the most responsive company in its field, so quick in the turnaround that some of its key suppliers, including Nodulex, were unable to keep pace. Determined to maintain its edge, Briktek was now kissing off such vendors. Briktek's impending desertion of Nodulex, Moore knew, had thrown the latter company into a final frenzy.

"Ann," concluded Headhunter, "it's pretty clear that Nodulex must remake itself the way Briktek did. You know how to do that because you helped do it at Briktek. Do it at Nodulex. Take the challenge."

You have to admire Headhunter, thought Moore. The guy knows just the right psychological buttons to push at just the right time. Headhunter correctly sensed that once her curiosity was piqued, Moore was virtually incapable of backing away from a challenge. With Moore tipping in his direction, Headhunter pushed a final button: "One more thing. I hesitate to mention this, but.... Never mind."

"You can't stop now," Moore replied.

"Well, okay. I don't know where you stand as a feminist, and I'm not supposed to ask. But strictly off the record, it would be a breath of fresh air for the whole industry and a publicity boost for Nodulex if someone like you became CEO. Talk about smashing a paradigm! I can see the trade headlines now: 'A NEW LOOK FOR AN OLD BUSINESS,' that sort of thing. I doubt if that has escaped the Nodulex board. Or you either, Ann."

"Right on both counts."

The publicity spotlight, however, had no allure for Ann Moore, whose inclination was to keep both her personal and professional lives private. Perhaps a little too private. She was still blushing over her inclusion in a recent *Philadelphia Magazine* article: "Young Executives Worth Watching." Given her seventeen years in the rat race, it was stretching a bit to call Moore a young executive. She was, however, competent, energetic and glamorous, prerequisites for any *Philadelphia* hit parade.

In the wake of the *Philadelphia* article, she had become an instant target for some of the city's glamorous corporate males, not all of whom were single and two of whom had also made the "Worth Watching" list. After two months of saying no, Moore was still unsure whether to be flattered or insulted by the attention. And now the Nodulex spotlight?

4

Although her brush with celebrity status had been a nuisance, Moore knew that whining about privacy was useless and unconvincing — especially after she took the Nodulex job. Or rather, *if* she took the Nodulex job.

First things first. "Okay," she told Headhunter. "Give them my name. Let's see how the interviews go."

While waiting for Nodulex to make the next move, and still unsure she was a viable candidate, Moore turned to the professional grapevine for an unofficial version of Nodulex history. Gradually, the story took form.

Nodulex owed its name to the fact that during World War II, its founders had developed the top-secret X Nodule, a technical breakthrough that caused a tiny, research-based operation to grow like a mushroom. In 1946, to capitalize on its status within the business community, Nodule Experts, Inc., trademarked 'Nodulex.' The company grew with the post-war consumer boom. So did corporate know-how. In the sixties, the Essington company's product had evolved into complex, multinodular modules, but the original name, still catchy, stuck.

Nodulex devices virtually eliminated slippage between a drive motor and its ultimate work. Properly applied, they prevented motor burnouts, gear breakage, spring wear, and other problems associated with precision, high-speed power reduction. Recent applications included analog computers, precision flow computers, and laser-controlled positioning tables.

For two decades, products manufactured by the company's Module Division found particular favor with the nearby giant Briktek, maker of a popular line of precision stepping motors. Equipped with Nodulex devices, Briktek motors were almost free from high-speed, high-torque burnout, a superior feature that did wonders for Briktek and Nodulex alike. Nodulex also supplied modules to a variety of other companies in several business sectors. Marketing was managed by a separate division whose task it was to forecast future demand and provide manufacturing direction.

During the seventies, Nodulex diversified, leveraging its know-how into precision controllers for bacteria-free, de-ionized water systems of the sort used at high-purity manufacturing sites. A Service Division was created to design such systems, which were purchased in advance by designers or by established plants seeking to update outmoded systems. Emphasizing high-quality service, the new division flourished by designing, installing, and providing long-term maintenance of clients' water systems on a turn-key basis. Most system subelements were manufactured by vendors using Nodulex designs.

The Service Division's ability to adapt its product to the varying needs of clients gave Nodulex a comfortable niche for several years. During the eighties, however, aggressive competitors invaded that niche. As the pace of contracting quickened, the Service Division struggled ineffectively to keep down costs and meet customers' hectic building schedules.

The company's traditions had not equipped it to move with changing times. Until the slump of the early nineties burst its bubble, Nodulex had accustomed itself to a comfortable work pace and a relaxed attitude about the future. Inside the company, that seductive mindset became known as "Comfortability" and was regarded as a cultural asset. Indeed, Comfortability proved to be an outright attraction for blue- and white-collar types who valued pleasant working conditions. The work force was racially and ethnically mixed, with African-, Italian-, and Ukrainian-Americans predominant among the rank and file. Most lived in nearby neighborhoods, but enough Nodulexers made the snarly commute from West Philadelphia and across the Walt Whitman Bridge from New Jersey to demonstrate that Comfortability counted. Labor strife was almost non-existent.

Management consisted largely of white males with local roots and long service records, most of whom lived in the concentric circles of suburbia surrounding greater Philadelphia. Turnover, both blue- and white-collar, was slight.

As Moore pieced together Nodulex history and culture, she wondered just how bad the outlook could be for so well-defined a company. The answer was very. For the last four years, with a payroll of about five hundred people and an overall total productivity measurement of $150,000 per employee, sales had been flat and profits were zero. The flat figure was $75 million, of which Modules comprised about $37 million. Service sales included $30 million in system installations and $8 million in maintenance contracts.

Moore needed no help reading between financial lines. But she continued to dig for scuttlebutt, and she struck gold with Arthur Baldwin, Briktek's talented director of research and development. Baldwin's position necessarily afforded him an insider's savvy about suppliers such as Nodulex. Learning of Moore's Nodulex candidacy, Baldwin readily offered to share his insights. In his spare time Baldwin was a dedicated skirtchaser and, as both knew, his interest in Moore was not strictly professional. All he asked (and, as it turned out, all he got) was dinner with Moore.

They met at an overdecorated French Restaurant in Head House Square. Dinner proved to be very pleasant and Baldwin proved to have Nodulex's number. He was also expressly eager to spare Moore a decision she might regret, so he minced no words. "When Nodulex ground to a halt," he began, "the board at first blamed general economic conditions. Once that rationale was accepted, it served to excuse the next year's stagnation, and the next. By 1992, however, the Lotzes had to face the fact that it was Nodulex, not the world at large, that was out of whack. The competition, especially Modulanswer, had a fabulous year in '92. Markets for modules and systems were expanding then and still are. Except at Essington.

"What really put the fear of God into Nodulex was Briktek's gradual defection. Once, while I was in Essington conferring with Nodulex designers, I saw a framed commemorative plaque hanging on the wall which read 'EVERY GOOD BRIKBAT HAS A HARD-WORKING MODULE BEHIND IT.' Interesting, huh? That plaque, which is probably still there, symbolized the long-term benefits Briktek and Nodulex shared. But it presumed that Nodulex was the secret of Briktek's success, which just wasn't so. Now that Briktek is on the fast track, we need vendors who are likewise. There are such vendors, Modulanswer for one. Meanwhile, Nodulex is still on the slow track. It looks to me as though it has no future with Briktek."

"Suppose," said Moore, "Nodulex got onto the fast track?"

"Hard to imagine. I doubt if they can. Confidentially, so do they. They have to move quicker, but they're afraid that if they speed up their processes, their quality will decline. Could be. Anyway, they've overslept far too long, so they may not have time to perform miracles. Be real careful when you talk to them, Ann. Care for an after-dinner cognac?"

Moore was nothing if not careful. Touched by the sincerity of Baldwin's concern but aware of his extracurricular agenda, Moore agreed to a cognac and then a quick departure. "We'll do this again sometime," she said vaguely. As a consolation prize, she flashed Baldwin the brilliant smile which, she knew, was one of her most winning attributes. The photo in *Philadelphia Magazine* hadn't begun to do it justice.

Four days later, fortified by Baldwin's report and reenforced by Donna Karan, Charles Jourdan, and Chanel, Moore sailed through her preliminary interview at Nodulex. At her second screening, the only rough spot came when Marc Lotz, board chairman and retiring CEO, asked her to name her weakest point as a candidate. "There are two," she replied. "I'm not an expert on modules, and I'm not an expert on water systems."

"That we know," said Lotz. "And your strongest point?"

"There are two," she answered. "I'm not an expert on modules, and I'm not an expert on water systems." Lotz smiled quizzically, so she continued: "The problems at Nodulex — the challenges, as you call them — aren't attributable to a shortage of subject-matter experts. From what I've seen, I'm convinced that your problems are generic: your processes are too complex and time-consuming, which prevents prompt response to customers. You may not believe this, but long cycle time also compromises quality. I saw the same thing at Briktek. You know the Briktek story; what happened there could happen here."

Judging from the smiles and nods all around, that was what Big Lotz and his committee wanted to hear. The meeting ended on a cordial note and the follow-up was little more than a formality. Much to her surprise, and in confirmation of *Philadelphia Magazine's* judgment, Ann Moore accepted the chief executive's position at Nodulex.

Moore's Friday afternoon departure from Briktek included an impromptu farewell party at which her colleagues did their best to hide their dismay at her decision. Arthur Baldwin, whose absence from the party surprised and disappointed her, sent her a glass paperweight inscribed "EVERY GOOD NODULEXER HAS A HARD-WORKING BRIKBATTER BEHIND HIM. OR HER!"

Moore's plan was to make her Nodulex debut the following Monday morning. At home over the weekend, her anxiety mounting, she pored over a hefty portfolio of the company's recent struggles.

There was a great deal to study, for Nodulex was awash in paper: management information system printouts, committee reports, task force studies, quality cell proposals, and a succession of consultants' assessments. She started with a chronological reading of Nodulex's Business Improvement Team reports. One by one, they told the story of a well-intentioned company's vain attempt to heal itself.

Heal itself from what? It was apparent that senior management had been unable to pinpoint the causes of the company's stagnation. Appearances suggested that Nodulex management had been dutiful and attentive. For example, long before it became a nationwide managerial fad, senior managers had embraced quality-mindedness. A full-time quality manager and a small staff of assistants busied themselves fixing various lapses, mostly in manufacturing. As for technical capability, it was apparent that Nodulex products were state-of-the-art. Meanwhile, the company enjoyed the good will of its work force and everyone was putting in a full day's work. The cost of materials had not gotten out of hand. Just the same, Nodulex was losing ground in expanding markets.

Something, somewhere, needed immediate attention. Accordingly, a top-level Business Improvement Team (BIT) had been created to identify, prioritize and attack problems. The BIT, it turned out, was a disappointing exercise in self-diagnosis and self-medication.

One conspicuous sore spot, Moore learned, was forecasting. Nodulex could not anticipate the needs of its customers accurately enough or far enough in advance to respond in timely fashion. The BIT thus concluded that more precise forecasts would provide a sharper, more cost-effective manufacturing plan. To that end, every Nodulex salesperson was instructed to forecast what he or she expected to sell. That input, refined by marketing management, was handed to the planning staff.

It didn't work. Because the new forecasting process was more complicated than the old, it took longer, which meant that sales people and staff alike had to peer farther and farther into the future. Salespeople, it turned out, were no better than staff planners at looking beyond the company's already overlong delivery cycle. And more than ever, salespeople were needed for sales, not distracting prophecies.

Round Two began when the BIT cracked down on costs, thinking that if the company could get back to the ratios it had enjoyed in profitable years, it would likewise recapture a sound operating base. This called for specific expertise. Each divisional manager and departmental subordinate was sternly admonished about the need for austerity and then turned loose to identify the fat in his or her domain, reporting back on how much could be trimmed. Time passed.

When the cost reports were in, the BIT was roundly surprised and disappointed. After careful analysis, virtually every manager had concluded that his or her particular outfit was drumhead tight and operating within budget. Slashing expenses was out of the question because each department was already battling an increasing backlog of tasks with inadequate resources. Far from cutting costs, many managers proposed that their budgets be increased to offset worsening business conditions. Clearly, authorizing managers to do their own analysis had been a mistake.

Round Three: The Business Improvement Team then resorted to a meticulous, account-by-account review of current budgets, comparing actual expenditures to the desired lower figure. That analysis revealed that under-budget operations were in danger of collapse, while those over budget were continuously being assigned tasks that exceeded their resources. In other words, budgets provided no qualitative data to illuminate the problem. The slide continued.

Round Four: The BIT switched to another cost-cutting approach: show-cause requests, a pathway which led to more disappointments and rude awakenings. When, for example, the team asked why the Advertising and Promotion Department's budget had increased 17 percent in a year, A&P responded that it had taken over the Nodulex mail room from Support Services, which saved the company 28 percent over the previous year. Then why, asked the BIT, was Support Service's budget 7 percent higher than last year's? The answer was that the department had installed a computer terminal service in its former mail room that was now saving Nodulex $7 million a year — more than enough to cover the increased expense. It was the same throughout the company: no culprits.

Reading these bleak summaries, Moore noticed the lonely voice of Hirtle Zwicker, Nodulex Quality Manager, crying in the bureaucratic wilderness. As the lowest-ranking member of the BIT, Zwicker had repeatedly insisted that Nodulex seek a quality solution. At one point, Zwicker had proposed that instead of reacting to occasional outbreaks of substandard quality, Nodulex "should set the industry standard by rooting out and destroying the causes of quality problems wherever they exist." His proposal went unheeded, however, because Nodulex rated its quality on a par with the competition's. Quality seemed to be the least of the company's worries.

The BIT changed its tune in 1993, when the sacred Briktek relationship fell into jeopardy. Marketing was learning the hard way that there was more to quality than a low defect rate and a low price. Briktek's purchasing manager made a personal presentation in Essington, pointing out that the definition of quality had grown more sophisticated. Zero defects and ironclad warranties? More than that. With the pace of business accelerating, he said, quality had come to mean rapid, precise response. For its own part, Briktek had lately streamlined its processes and now operated almost flawlessly on very short cycle time. Those who supplied Briktek must do likewise.

Although Briktek put it nicely, the writing was on the wall: Despite its dependability and affordability, Nodulex was proving unable to respond acceptably to Briktek's accelerated pace and frequently changing mix of orders. Other suppliers could keep up, however, and for that Briktek was willing to pay extra. By way of confirmation, Briktek awarded the entire module contract for Brikantine, an auspicious new motor it had brought to market in record time, to Modulanswer, Inc.

Panic time at Nodulex, thought Moore as she finished the Briktek report. In her mind's eye she could see office lights burning late in Essington as the company thrashed about for a quick solution.

Nodulex's subsequent search for quick solutions were embodied in a stack of consultant reports that provided more interesting weekend reading. Out of home remedies by the end of 1991, Nodulex threw itself on the mercy of outside experts, beginning with the Quaker City Consulting Group, a prestigious firm that unleashed dozens of MBAs inside the Essington plant and charged accordingly. After several months of study, QCCG summed up Nodulex's predicament:

- Nodulex was not making any money.

- Nodulex was losing market share.

- Quality was at best equal to, not above, industry standards.

- Manufacturing costs were too high.

- Company morale was slipping because of overall poor performance.

11

The only surprise in this costly report was that competitors had eliminated Nodulex's onetime quality edge. Two clear objectives were indicated, said QCCG: The company should somehow slim down its processes, and it should achieve quality standards that outdistanced all competitors.

Knowing QCCG's high rates, Moore could not help reflecting that her grandmother could have delivered the same sort of common-sense analysis, only cheaper and faster. But QCCG also recommended solutions. Nodulex should:

- undertake a top-to-bottom, high-energy quality improvement program sparked by heavy doses of corporate inspiration

- improve sales through an aggressive new sales and advertising campaign

- consider a 10 percent across-the-board reduction in headcount

- automate as much as possible to achieve an immediate surge in quality and, eventually, more cost-effective production

- dramatize the importance of the new objectives by bringing in from outside a new CEO who would personify a more hopeful future.

The QCCG people offered to design and oversee the necessary programs, but the Nodulex board decided to go it alone using selected consultants for guidance. Thus began a succession of experts, each of whom peddled a special remedy: structural reform, software packages, statistical process control, and people involvement.

The first of these set out to "de-layer" the organization, contending that if Nodulex management compressed its chain of command, decisions and results could move faster up and down the line with no compromise in quality or performance. The idea was aesthetically attractive; but when implemented, de-layering produced no measurable improvement in the company fortunes. No one could determine exactly why.

Next came a consultant bent on revamping Nodulex's management information system. He installed new software which upgraded the system, giving it the capability to gather and disseminate a dazzling array of data. But the upgrade did not translate into more competitive performance — another mysterious disappointment. What it did translate into was a paralyzing mountain of data and reams of reports.

Desperate at this point, the company re-examined its market position, seeking to differentiate itself from competitors. Lower prices? Out of the question. Nodulex prices were as low as anyone's, and there was no wiggle room in that area because of the profit picture. Higher quality? Bingo! Offering a product a cut above industry standards would surely restore momentum, volume, and eventually, profits. The Module Division was authorized to undertake a quality improvement program to be designed by an outside consultant and administered inside Nodulex by Quality Manager Zwicker.

That effort, at long last, created a bright spot. Like most quality improvement programs, Zwicker's adopted the view that improved quality would pay for itself and differentiate the company from its competitors. Called "Back On Track," the program began on a gala, upbeat note and appeared to have staying power. Within the troubled Module Division, painstaking inspections at several points on the manufacturing line cut the defect rate, permitting the company to boast that it produced the most rigidly monitored, defect-free units in the industry. According to a press release issued just a week before, the company's current hope for a turn-around was "based on Back On Track and the guidance of its newly-acquired CEO, Ann Moore."

When she read that release late on the Saturday before she took the Nodulex helm, Moore was momentarily seized by an image of the *Titanic*, stern high in the air, heading for the bottom. And I'm the skipper, she thought, teetering on the brink of panic.

Moore's panic had moderated two days later when she officially assumed command. Her first week at Essington was repeatedly interrupted by the hushed congratulations of her staff and, on Friday afternoon, by an interview with a business reporter from the *Philadelphia Inquirer*, prematurely scheduled by an overeager Nodulex publicist. Damn! Nothing like starting with a bang, thought Moore as the reporter entered. What could she say so early in the game?

Despite her aversion to publicity, Moore's personality was decidedly media-friendly, and she used it to advantage with the visiting journalist.

Brimming with nervous energy, she punctuated her conversation by verbally italicizing key words and by flashing the formidable smile already known around the office as The Headlight. Holding forth behind an antique desk in her Nodulex office, she seemed the very image of fast-track success. Her remodeled lair overlooking the asphalt and sumac was a startling pocket of good taste and a dramatic contrast to the cluttered, knockabout environment just outside the door. The sole office decorations were a pair of antique copper running-horse weathervanes mounted on the wall behind her desk and a similarly old, sculptural gull decoy resting on a glass-topped coffee table surrounded by a suede sofa and chairs. No greenery, real or artificial, was to be seen, and her desktop was devoid of personal photographs. The office had the understated, disciplined look of success. Too disciplined, perhaps.

To emphasize her impressive credentials gracefully, Moore assured the reporter that she had been through the executive mill: "I considered myself topped out when I became Briktek's chief financial officer seven years ago. Then I got a chance to come here, which offers me a new world of hands-on experience. I intend to use the techniques here that worked for me in my last position."

Briktek's miracle had been big news in Philadelphia, and the reporter was well acquainted with the story. "Do I understand," he said, "that Nodulex is going to get the same system Briktek used to beat the Japanese?"

"Right. Briktek adopted a culture called Total Cycle Time, with which it improved its response to customers, shortened its development time on new products, and maximized the productivity of people and equipment using minimal resources. We'll do that here as well, because the quality problems Nodulex has are imbedded in the company's processes just as they were at Briktek."

"I understand that quality has already taken a turn for the better here," said the reporter.

"It has. But I'm convinced that Nodulex's approach to date hasn't *begun* to tap its quality potential. My approach presumes that quality improvement accelerates as cycle times shorten. Nodulex needs to address its cycle times, because cycle times drive this business. Every business.

"I'm not just talking about manufacturing cycle time. We've got to simplify processes, blue- and white-collar, throughout the company — a total approach. We can become quality leaders if our processes are in order. I have my work cut out for me." The interviewer seemed to sense that here was an issue worth exploring further, but his time, unfortunately,

14

was up. Moore was overdue for her first formal meeting with staffers, a few of whom were now visible in the outer office, darting nervous glances at their new boss through her half-opened door. The topic for the upcoming meeting was of course quality. "Talk with me again," she said to the reporter, flashing The Headlight and proffering a firm handshake. "This story is worth following up."

"One last question. Where did you acquire your expertise in modules and high-purity systems?"

A loaded question, but Moore took it: "There's already enough expertise here to run several companies. I have a different set of assets. My know-how is *generic*. Nodulex's underlying quality problems are likewise generic. In addition, I'm an outsider. I can probably spot obstructive attitudes and practices that expert insiders have overlooked. Getting and keeping first-rate quality requires a lot more than a specialized approach. Until next time... thanks!"

One of the middle-aged males now edging into Moore's office was quality manager Hirtle "Zwick" Zwicker, who overheard that last comment and felt an apprehensive chill. Might Moore have said what she did for his benefit? If she called upon him for moral support during the forthcoming meeting, what would he say? Zwick hadn't a clue. What he did have was an armful of data on defect reduction in module manufacturing, clear evidence that Nodulex was making progress toward its goal. Might as well make a good first impression on the new boss.

As the meeting opened, Moore passed around a one-page profile of Nodulex:

Sales	$75.0 million
People cost	22.5 million
Material cost	37.5 million
Inventory Carrying Cost	6.0 million
Other costs	9.0 million
Inventory	30.0 million
Profit	$0.0.

"This outline," said Moore, "reveals a company in real trouble." No Headlight.

15

Moore continued: "Before you assure me that those figures represent honest effort by people working very hard, let me tell you I know that is true. I *also* know that Nodulex is no different from any other company with a long history and a distinctive character" — Moore omitted any reference to Comfortability — "so these figures you've been battling to achieve have nothing to do with what we can and will achieve. At Briktek, we achieved our entitled level of competitive quality using a systematic method: Total Cycle Time. What worked there will work here.

"The numbers you're looking at represent Nodulex's baseline performance. Forget them, because I'm not here to achieve an incremental improvement over baseline. I'm here — and so are you, now — to help Nodulex achieve its *entitled* performance. The company's entitlement is so far above baseline that I won't jeopardize my credibility with an estimate at this point. But based on my Briktek experience, I'll tell you this: In product and service quality, customer satisfaction and effective use of resources, Nodulex can do a lot better. And will."

Zwick broke the silence that followed: "Excuse me, wasn't this meeting supposed to address quality issues?"

"You bet," replied Moore. "*Big* quality issues."

Uh-oh, thought Zwick and associates. This is gonna be a long one.

COMMENTARY

Chapter One

Quality and Substance

As Ann Moore learned, Nodulex had spent years barking up the wrong trees in search of competitiveness. By the time she came on board, the company's very survival was at stake. Survival and competitiveness are both a matter of pleasing customers, who must be confident that the products and services they pay for are the best that circumstances allow. That being the case, Nodulex was correct to identify quality improvement as a major component of survival. It is the customer who casts the deciding vote on whether a product's quality is up to snuff; and Nodulex customers were voting with their feet.

The company's chances of surviving and competing were only as good as its quality program, which had enjoyed some initial success in reducing defects. But would lower defect rates suffice to satisfy customers and restore competitiveness? Almost certainly not.

In most endangered companies, quality shortcomings are more profound, more subtle, than anyone suspects. That is why so many quality improvement programs, which attack specific problems, stall or fail altogether. At Nodulex, the record of tortuous, unrewarding self-medication and the successive array of consultant "solutions" suggested that the company's quality crisis ran deeper than defects or reliability rates.

Nodulex was by no means an unusual example. Most quality programs are long on form and short on substance, and therefore deal ineffectively with root causes. Consequently, whatever results they deliver are not meaningful to the customer or the bottom line. By and large, such programs are ruinously expensive and wasteful of time and resources. In strategic terms, they are at cross purposes to their stated objective.

Which is not to say that they are not at first popular. Better quality is a motherhood issue, so few oppose it in principle. Furthermore, the notion that quality pays for itself in the long run is widely accepted, so the effort it entails does not arouse controversy — not, at least, at the outset. And results such as Nodulex's initial reduction in defects seem to indicate better things to come. Beware.

The popular assumption that quality comes free needs to be re-examined. In many cases, incremental improvements do not begin to pay the cost of a quality program. Meanwhile, teams are formed, paperwork accumulates and people are distracted — without any measurable bottom-line result.

Quality and Competitiveness

The first step toward meaningful quality improvement is to realize that quality and competitiveness are inextricably linked. In any business, be it manufacturing or service, high-quality, competitive performance requires internal processes that are as simple and seamless as possible. Few companies even come close to that objective.

Looking at the symptoms of decline at Nodulex, it is apparent that the company got into trouble because its processes were out of control: too complicated, too costly, too time consuming. Ironically, the corporate culture of Comfortability, which was a source of internal pride, virtually guaranteed that problems would go from bad to worse. By the time Nodulex awoke to the competitiveness crisis of the late 1980s, traditional measurements of quality and competitiveness were long gone. Windows of opportunity had shortened, everyday expectations had become more exacting, and competition was getting keener by the day. Briktek, Nodulex's chief customer, measured quality in terms of timely response. Thus, unless Nodulex could reduce its cycle time commensurate with improved product quality, the latter achievement would be meaningless.

Suddenly alarmed and desperate for a turnaround, Nodulex behaved like many other threatened companies, taking a well-worn path to disaster. First came reflexive approaches to business improvement, the gist of which were to apply additional resources so that the faulty system could be optimized. Next came the cost-cutting backlash, which revealed how company leadership was compartmented into functional silos, each of which deemed itself blameless. Then came the quest for outside miracle-workers.

The Nodulex experience illustrates the fact that no company can survive, much less achieve top quality, without simple, seamless business processes and a cultural mindset that demands continuous improvement. Such conditions are attainable only through systematic inspection of every work cycle within a business and the elimination of steps that obstruct the shortest possible cycle time. In a short-cycle-time company, quality occurs naturally.

Competitiveness and quality are intertwined, but it is the former, not the latter, that drives a business. Quality is a function of competitive business processes, not vice versa. Short cycle times are indicators of orderly processes. Orderly processes are indicators of high product quality. Today's customers define quality as a full spectrum of services including precise response, freedom from hassle, timely delivery, and defect-free products, all of which can be achieved only through orderly, streamlined business processes.

A company that has achieved short cycle time in all its processes — Total Cycle Time — is by definition a company with high-quality products or services.

There are countless real-world examples of how well-managed, sophisticated companies overlook the root causes of their quality and competitiveness problems. Here is one, provided by my colleague, Arthur Skeats, who assisted a Texas manufacturer of aircraft components in its struggle to improve quality. As Arthur put it, "The CEO already knew that quality alone was not enough. He was an FAA-certified producer, but smaller competitors were taking more [market] share due to his long make/market cycle time. He wanted to increase responsiveness to keep his customers. Quality was a 'given' in this industry — cycle time had become the differentiator."

To improve performance in a way meaningful to customers, the company reorganized its production flow, abandoning functional structure in favor of just-in-time production cells. Work teams inside the cells volunteered for assignments and managed themselves. "Cycle time was the primary driver from the program start," recalled Arthur. To measure its progress, the company monitored cycle time, defect rates, the number of production steps, and the distance material traveled during production. It eventually cut its cycle time by 50 percent, its number of steps by 45 percent, and its material travel distance by 75 percent. Result? The revitalized company now had unbeatable responsiveness and was positioned for market dominance.

Quality, Competitiveness, and The Three R's

A truly competitive Total Cycle Time company possesses three prerequisites for survival. I call them the Three R's:

1. Responsiveness — the ability to satisfy customers' needs quickly and precisely. The word "satisfy" is key here because customer satisfaction is a critical component of high-quality performance. Relentlessly reducing cycle time in every part of a business will engender a quick, precise response to customer needs.

2. Results acceleration — the ability to use feedback from past performance to simplify and quicken a process without working harder or adding resources. This procedure, known as Cycles of Learning, becomes especially effective as cycle times shorten and the flow of feedback increases accordingly.

3. Resource effectiveness — the ability to obtain superior results using available (or even fewer) resources. Resource effective ness has a particularly strong impact upon the utilization of people as well as cash tied up in inventory and receivables. It is achieved by systematically abolishing unnecessary actions in every cycle and subcycle of activity.

No operation can justifiably praise its quality or competitiveness unless all of the Three R's are present. When, as at Briktek, they are in place, a company is almost certainly performing at its entitled level, which can be a world away from its former, baseline expectations. And there is a strategic payoff: At entitlement, windows of opportunity undreamed of at baseline suddenly open.

In the case of Nodulex, none of the Three R's were in place; quite the contrary, in fact. Customers were demanding faster response. Company forecasters could not see beyond the long cycle times. Cycles of Learning were few, and when managers sought to improve performance, they habitually asked for additional resources.

Barriers to Effective Performance

Once Nodulex had been rudely awakened, a Business Improvement Team took action. Its attempted remedies, however, ran counter to the Three R's, adding barriers to better performance instead of removing them. In today's business climate, that syndrome is often fatal.

Why are barrier-filled, long cycle times so prevalent? Because, left to its own devices, every business accumulates bad habits that lengthen cycle time and obstruct high-quality, competitive performance. Most of these barriers are actions in process which complicate work without adding value to the completed task. When freed of such obstructions, work cycles become correspondingly short and uncomplicated, which promotes error-free activity, effective use of resources, and quick results.

Virtually everyone who has held a job can recall some procedure that needlessly complicated tasks, or made office life tedious, or put a much-needed decision on hold. Roadblocks like those are easy to spot, but they are not the most sinister. More formidable barriers to quality and competitiveness lie unchallenged beneath the surface of everyday affairs.

These major barriers are the inevitable by-product of corporate growth and change. Almost all are enacted in good faith and seemed to make sense at the time. Once legitimized in practice, they remain in force regardless of their value to the overall operation. A company with overlong cycle times tolerates an environment in which things can go wrong. A company whose cycle times are unresponsive to customer needs cannot provide quality service.

Most serious barriers to effective performance are related to the business process. Redundant paperwork is a classic example; so are overzealous data tracking, illogically placed equipment, ongoing inspections that new equipment has made unnecessary, emergency procedures that remain in place after a crisis has passed, and obsolete measurements that were not abolished when new ones took their place. All of us have our own set of pet peeves which, for the sake of better performance, should be subjected forthwith to the Three R's test.

In large companies, especially white-collar environments, business process barriers are part of the everyday routine. Most people come to terms with them and accept them without protest. Many process barriers live on inside a company because internal myopia has rendered them invisible. At Nodulex, the deeply felt values of Comfortability blinded people to its harmful effects.

Comfortability is an example of a cultural barrier. Because cultural barriers are integral components of company thinking, they are the most pernicious. They are also the hardest to uproot and destroy. I will have more to say about the nature of barriers and their removal later in this book. Meanwhile, a closer look at Nodulex's struggles is in order.

Quality and Performance: Self-Medication

Nodulex's failure to heal itself from within should come as no surprise to anyone familiar with short-cycle-time thinking. The company was probably foredoomed by its own cultural myopia: It simply lacked the intellectual objectivity to spot root causes of decline.

Take the forecasting "problem." Management's response to inaccurate forecasts was to lengthen the forecasting cycle by adding new steps to the process. More resources were poured in to no effect because the company was treating the symptoms of a problem (imprecision) instead of its causes (overlong cycle times, which pushed effective forecasting into the realm of clairvoyance). Instead of tinkering with the forecasting mechanism, Nodulex would have been better advised to shorten its delivery cycle so that forecasters need not squint into a distant, uncertain future.

Or take the cost-cutting issue. The desperate spate of show-cause requests through which Nodulex chased its own tail served only to dramatize the tangle of organizational interleaving that had grown naturally during good times. Despite the effort, Nodulex was totally unable to bring expenses into line because it attacked "expenses" as a series of separate, isolated problems. The true enemies of progress were long, barrier-laden cycle times, which went unchallenged. Meanwhile, more time was wasted.

Quality and Performance: Calling in the Consultants

The one positive aspect of the consultant cavalcade at Nodulex was the BIT's realization that insiders were too subjective, too close to the company's problems, to spot key barriers.

Consultants are outsiders sure enough, but they are also apt to sell a prepackaged cure, not a customized solution. Structural de-layering, for example, optimized Nodulex's organizational structure within the context of its existing — dysfunctional — processes. There was no meaningful improvement because structure is not an important determinant of competitive performance. Cycle time is.

The consultant who upgraded the management information systems hoped to smooth out the process. The result? A state-of-the-art method that provided more data with which to mismanage the company. Nodulex's quality improvement program, also designed by an outside consultant, showed the most promise because it at least attacked process barriers harmful to quality. Its full impact, which forms the body of Chapter Two, had yet to be felt when Moore stepped into the CEO's slot.

Nodulex and the Baseline Mentality

In its attempts to turn itself around, Nodulex had made three fundamental errors. The first was to assume that raw determination, unassisted by an outside perspective, can root out barriers to better performance. That just isn't so, because insiders are accustomed to the baseline attitudes, oversights, redundant procedures, and wrong measurements that compromise quality and performance.

The second mistake occurred when the company at last realized it needed an outside perspective. At that point, the temptation to go for a quick cure and, when that failed, another, then another, was irresistible.

Management's third mistake was to think incrementally. Throughout its struggles, Nodulex hoped for a modest percentage of improvement over baseline. Those piecemeal approaches were like buckets of water dumped into the sea. No one sensed that total, fundamental changes were necessary: cultural change, process change, attitude change, measurement change. By way of contrast, Briktek had learned that achieving competitive quality required total abandonment of baseline thinking and a thrust toward the very best that could be achieved on existing resources — entitlement. At entitlement, Briktek now operated so responsively that Nodulex's vendorship was threatened.

Ann Moore, who expected to leverage her Briktek expertise to remake Nodulex's business processes and culture, had her work cut out for her. The Comfortability mindset was entrenched. Meanwhile, the Back On Track quality program's headway seemed to promise a boost in business, morale and the company's slipping image.

Time would tell — if there was any time left.

Chapter Two

The Quality Game

As Hirtle Zwicker had feared, that first meeting with the new CEO turned out to be a long one. Worse, it gave him a creepy feeling that the quality campaign he had been leading at Nodulex was about to crash and burn. Ann Moore did almost all of the talking, leaving Zwick no time to ballyhoo the company's upward progress.

Although she seldom made direct eye contact with anyone and her body language revealed a case of opening-night jitters, Moore quickly established a no-nonsense, no-optimism mood. Her wide-ranging comments, laced with arcane terminology, amounted to a critique of Nodulex's present performance, which she repeatedly labeled "baseline," a term that seemed to belittle the company's diligence. Eventually, she came to her own definition of quality improvement; but by then, Zwick's mind was wandering and his morale slipping. Putting it nicely, the bottom-line message was that the new boss was mightily unimpressed.

Moore's somber, jumpy remarks left no doubt that management was now on notice and that Zwick and the attending VPs should probably put their summer vacation plans on hold. Aw, no! Literally on the eve of a well-deserved, much-anticipated getaway, Zwick realized he was stuck. That seemed unfair because, generally speaking, module quality was better than ever and still improving. Furtively, he peeled off three Tums tablets from the roll he kept in his scuffed briefcase and began steeling himself for a sweltering August in Philly.

Sure enough, when the meeting broke up well past quitting time,

Moore gingerly touched Zwick on the arm and said she would need to see him first thing Monday morning. Zwick of course said nothing about his mangled vacation plans.

Zwicker family vacations had always occurred like clockwork at a white clapboard farmhouse on the south shore of Nova Scotia. Becky Zwicker, who taught pre-school, spent her entire summer there with the kids; Zwick went up for his allotted three weeks each August. For Zwick, who lived in a crumbling West Philadelphia neighborhood of elderly, identical row houses, these predictable, idyllic summer getaways had enormous emotional importance. For one thing, they differentiated him from the rest of the middle management horde he faced every day. In all his years at Nodulex, Zwick had met no one who had been to Nova Scotia and few who knew where to find it, which was okay with him. Traveling such a distance was a royal pain, he would admit to friends whose idea of a getaway was an Atlantic City casino or a worn-out, South Jersey seashore resort. How could such people appreciate that the view from his window on Bell Island took in a breathtaking, bracing, fragrant chunk of flowered meadow, rocky, wooded shore, and the Atlantic Ocean — all his? They couldn't, he decided, so he kept quiet about that part of his world. But he had been hooked for years.

Because his parents had emigrated from Nova Scotia before he was born and he still had relatives in Lunenburg County, Zwick called the house on Bell Island "the ancestral homestead," although it was not. It was in fact a retreat he had bought for a song in the late sixties, just after graduating from college. Back then, the draft was breathing down his neck, and, as a diehard opponent of the Vietnam War, he was determined not to serve, even if it meant moving to Canada. Time, marriage, and his first child resolved that dilemma, but ever since, he and his family had spent summers refurbishing the house, straightening the sagging barn and puttering among the property's woods, fields and shoreline.

After each vacation, Zwick returned to Philly completely revitalized, a few pounds heavier, his fair skin pink and peeling, ready to mount the quality barricade for another year. You couldn't put a price on that kind of vacation — not until this year. What really hurt was that this year would be the last family getaway before his twin daughters went off to college and, presumably, lives of their own. After that, who knew?

Zwick's hair was growing thinner, his middle thicker, and he had begun to feel his years. With early retirement looking better by the day, he now thought seriously of spending his "sunset years" on Bell Island, although he knew it was too soon to mention this idea to Becky. Nova Scotia was a side of Zwick's life quite separate and secret from his career yet crucial to his professional well-being. The mere thought of that tranquil spot could bring a contented smile to his lips during the most grueling, boring days on the job. Until now.

Zwick spent the weekend at home in his Barcalounger, prepping for Monday's meeting with Ann Moore and reviewing the decline of Nodulex while his muted TV flashed silent play-by-plays. Going over the last couple of years, he had to admit that until the Back On Track quality program was launched, he had put in quite a few boring, unchallenging years at Nodulex. Not that he was complaining. The first of his family to reach white-collar status, Zwick had always moderated his professional goals. His ego was sized to his ambition, so he found it easy to efface himself before the corporate structure he served. When, nine years ago, he completed a training course and became the company's quality manager, he had felt the warm blanket of a permanent sinecure envelop him.

He had, however, done his level best to promote the importance of quality to the company's long-range success. But most of the time, he and his team burned midnight oil analyzing and fixing someone's preventable lapse from standard. Nodulex bigwigs liked to talk about running a quality operation but, by and large, they understood very little.

As a consequence, one important thing had been missing from Zwick's professional life: recognition for his achievement. He saw himself correctly as an unprepossessing personality, someone who turned up here or there around the plant with rolled-up shirtsleeves and a perpetually rumpled appearance. Everyone referred to him simply as Zwick; few Nodulexers outside of Accounting even knew his real name. The most he could say for his standing at Nodulex was that he helped keep the wheels turning and was always consulted when defect rates rose or too many customers complained. Lip service notwithstanding, Nodulex managers considered quality an issue outside their everyday concerns, an antibiotic resorted to in a pinch to make sick operations get better. Zwick, who dispensed the antibiotic, had not been able to crack that mindset.

Suddenly, his world had changed when, attempting to reverse its decline, the BIT got serious about quality and called in a consultant to design a formal improvement program. That consultant peddled a five-point corporate objective which, among other things, would propel Hirtle Zwicker to stage center of the company's comeback plan:

1. Management and staff must learn to live by the rule that quality was a permanent necessity, not an attractive frill. Everyone must understand that quality paid for itself by driving competitiveness. A training program was prepared to institutionalize the new thinking among managers.

2. From top to bottom, Nodulexers must be persuaded that quality-mindedness is everyone's responsibility. Accordingly, training would eventually fan out to all levels of the company.

3. Because quality was everyone's business, teams at all levels and specialties within the organization would be assembled to uncover pockets of "unquality," make formal recommendations about remedial action and, when authorized by management, supervise corrections. Nodulex's own Hirtle Zwicker would coordinate these efforts.

4. To dramatize the importance of quality, Nodulex must be able to measure the cost of unquality. The consultant installed a series of accounting practices for that purpose which tracked the costs of lost sales, rework, fixing customer complaints, and maintaining quality people on the payroll. Presumably, as quality rose, these costs would decline, demonstrating a measurable benefit.

5. Inspiration was essential to maximize the effectiveness of quality improvement. Accordingly, the company's program must receive a momentous kickoff.

Zwick still felt a twinge of excitement as he recalled how Consultant helped him rough out his plan for that momentous kickoff. Its keynote phrase, "Back On Track," would convey urgency and optimism. Its atmosphere would be festive and upbeat — a party, really. It would involve everyone in the company and it would emphasize top management's personal commitment to change. Consultant's parting words to Zwick were these: "Quality is a feel-good issue; nobody's against it. Take the positive approach instead of harping on shortcomings. Get people on your side. Give them a kickoff party they'll remember. Pull out the emotional stops so everyone can bond with the issue. And keep up the publicity. After awhile, the results will start speaking for themselves! Oh, and don't sell yourself short. Back On Track will make you the company's quality czar and you must be prepared to use that empowerment."

Wow! Whereupon Consultant bade farewell to Quality Czar Hirtle Zwicker in the Nodulex parking lot, assuring him that he was "just a phone call away." After presenting his enormous bill (which scandalized Zwick despite management's okay), he whooshed away in his shiny black Porsche.

Well, thought Nodulex's quality czar, leaning against his dented blue Bronco, let the games begin.

The games began with a bang three weeks later (and six months before Nodulex switched CEOs). Preparing the Back On Track kickoff, Zwick had a lot of willing help from corporate PR and personnel staffers, all of whom readily appreciated the importance of getting instant consensus. Consultant had spoken the truth; Zwick did indeed have clout.

The company shot the works on a massive, inspirational, all-hands gathering at Essington's Corinthian Yacht Club, a gracious, elite survivor of earlier times whose well-tended groves and dignified facilities were a world apart from the gritty module plant just a few hundred yards away. Most Nodulexers had never set foot in the yacht club until Back On Track's trumpet sounded.

Things went beautifully. The event was spread over two working days to accommodate various shifts. By bussing Nodulex people to and from the yacht club, the company prevented commuters from playing hooky. Having received a week's advance notice and an explanation of the gathering, each shift assembled in the Corinthian parking lot facing a platform festooned with blue-and-gold pennants bearing the company logo and an immense banner proclaiming "QUALITY AND COMPETITIVE-NESS — WE'RE BACK ON TRACK!" Energetic music for the occasion was supplied by the Essington Stompers, Nodulex's own six-piece

Dixieland band. Following a fanfare from the Stompers, the company's aging CEO and chairman, Marc Lotz (who headed the clan of company owners and was duly known as "Big Lotz") gave a forceful, mercifully short speech prepared for him by PR people on the importance of a formal quality program. The divisional VPs did likewise in their turn, legitimizing Back On Track with management's visible stamp of approval.

Then it was Zwick's turn at the mike. The new quality czar, whose forte was not speechmaking, had spent several nights honing his remarks with Becky as a captive audience. An underachieving nonentity in high school and college, he was intimidated by the kickoff's carefully orchestrated, pep-rally atmosphere; but when the moment of truth arrived, he mustered enough vim and volume to elicit hearty whistles and applause. "Your name is now a household word in Essington!" Big Lotz said to Zwick after the round of pep talks had been completed. "Time for a drink!"

Speeches over, everyone was treated to a sumptuous outdoor barbecue lubricated by enough cold beer to float a light cruiser. During the meal, all hands were issued a packet containing a handsome enameled lapel pin that could double as a tie tack, bearing the quality program's official title superimposed on the image of a charging steam locomotive. The packet also enclosed similarly designed bumper stickers, decals, and a wallet-sized card bearing on one side a condensed version of the program's rationale and on the other, in boldface, the assurance that quality was everyone's business.

As a closer, Zwick stepped again to the platform mike and asked the sated Nodulexers to don their pins as an act of solidarity. It was a corny gesture that seemed to work. Most complied, and quite a few even managed a round of applause before loudspeakered good-nights closed the proceedings and the Stompers played a farewell number.

Later, Zwick watched with surprised satisfaction as the last shuttle bus tail lights receded down the yacht club's tree-lined lane. He was further gratified that almost no castoff packets littered the area. So much for inspiration, he thought. Now for the hard part.

The hard part came easier than Zwick expected, however. Over the next several weeks, he religiously followed Consultant's guideline, going first for "low-hanging fruit": quick, conspicuous improvements that could be publicized to boost morale. He started where he could do the most good, on the Module Division's production line. Meanwhile, to keep sales volume respectable, Marketing cut prices. When, as expected, Nodulex quality became the industry standard, prices were to be raised.

Zwick's quality team determined that during manufacture, too many defective modules evaded on-line detection. Some were snagged at the last minute, necessitating time-consuming rework. Others were rejected by increasingly peeved customers whose cycle times were lengthened by waiting for a correction. Because the Module Division could not keep every customer waiting indefinitely, it had stockpiled an enormous inventory from which to replace defective units. Zwick expected to make a measurable improvement in that area. It stood to reason that reducing on-line defects would simplify the manufacturing process, thereby making Nodulex more responsive to customers. It would also help lower the colossal inventory.

To accomplish his objective, Zwick was ready to retrain manufacturing people to assume a more painstaking approach to production. Meanwhile, he enacted more painstaking inspections than the ones already in place. To ensure loyalty to the new quality goals, the manufacturing inspectors were placed under Zwick's authority, renamed the Back On Track Team, and given intensive instruction. Inspirational decor was added to the airy, lofty room housing the module line. The banner used at the kickoff party was suspended crosswise from the ceiling in view of every line worker. Each inspector wore blue-and-gold locomotive logos sewn on his or her smock. Zwick also saw to it that each issue of *Modularities*, the company newsletter, carried squibs about quality efforts and results.

Surprised by the strength of his own inspiration, Zwick was willing, even eager, to work longer and harder hours. He developed a series of intricate, detailed defect criteria forms to be completed by an inspector whenever a defect raised its ugly head. One intent of the forms was to provide a data base from which to refine precise quality standards; the other was to get a handle on the cost of unquality — hard numbers that would dramatize for top management the blood tax Nodulex was paying. As the team caught more and more defects, the cost-of-unquality figures likewise rose to sobering heights. Cutting defects would save Nodulex those costs.

Zwick got results. Already seasoned at their jobs, and clearly savoring their new freedom from manufacturing supervisors, Back On Track inspectors caught more than their former number of on-line defects. As a consequence, quality did indeed go up within the Module Division. Zwick was now confident that quality-mindedness had turned a corner at Nodulex and that the company had found the pathway back to competitiveness. Gone were the days of piecemeal first aid and lip service. The new, expanded quality team had earned legitimate status within the organization and was here to stay.

Another principle of Back On Track was that quality was everybody's business. To Zwick, that idea was not a mere maxim but a working guideline. Why not directly involve as many Nodulexers as possible in the quality process? Armed with written authorization from the company's Business Improvement Team, Zwick met with Module Division managers and line supervisors. Together they divided the work force into functionally-based cells of three to twelve individuals. The members of each cell were presumably expert in their sector of the module-making process and therefore optimally equipped to spot areas of potential improvement.

Thirty-six cells were set up within the division. Members of each cell were trained in brainstorming techniques and asked to meet biweekly. Their mission was to identify twelve ways to improve quality within their particular functional sector and to prepare implementation plans on a one-page form devised for the purpose. Zwick and his team would then review, prioritize, and authorize the proposals.

The new cells generated an amazing, heartening degree of employee enthusiasm. One month (two meetings) later, every cell submitted its quota of proposals. Ideas ranged from requests for housekeeping brooms to appeals for expensive new equipment, but each idea was in the spirit of achieving higher quality. After two more months had elapsed (during which the list of proposed actions continued to grow), Zwick had the initial proposals prioritized and approved. If no outlandish expense was involved, each cell got the go-ahead for its topmost item. When that was in place, each cell would move to its second priority, working down from there. Complex proposals were routed through the BIT with the quality team's endorsement. As creative ideas literally piled up on his desk, Zwick wondered why he hadn't thought of this before.

Zwick then began to consider ways to leverage Back On Track to improve the company's public image. To that end, he got support from Marketing VP Gerald Baker. Quality and Marketing people quickly agreed that the way to grab favorable public attention was to refine a product so reliable and defect-free that its image would put all of Nodulex's products in a more favorable light. The vehicle for this scheme was a proposed line of "Hi-Rel" modules aimed at aerospace applications and built to ultimate quality specifications.

Taking the ball, Gerry Baker involved Howard Lotz, Module Division VP, in the concept, and a special Hi-Rel manufacturing line was created. At Zwick's insistence, every phase of the operation, from the unpacking of new material to the packing of finished product, would undergo inspection by specially trained and certified quality people. The Hi-Rel line would require twice the number of employees necessary to produce garden-variety modules. Very costly for sure, but the results would justify the cost. Meanwhile, Hi-Rel had united Marketing and Module people in a clearly defined, challenging effort.

Months of preparation followed. Hi-Rel inspectors, who underwent additional hours of hands-on training and lectures by a certified government inspector, were graduated only if all the units they approved during a lengthy shakedown were absolutely perfect. Rejects would be reworked as necessary or scrapped; no compromises, no statistical excuses. Consequently, Nodulex could advertise Hi-Rel as "The Ultimate in Quality and Reliability in the Entire Industry," a boast which, given the care taken in its production, no competitor could match.

Zwick expected Hi-Rel to create a trickle-down effect, stimulating higher morale and quality-mindedness throughout the division. Divisional VP Howie Lotz was not so confident. Lotz was convinced that Hi-Rel would generate an abnormally high reject rate, so he stipulated that it must be treated as a pilot program under Zwick's direct authority, divorced from (and not chargeable against) the everyday performance of the Module Division.

To Zwick, Lotz appeared to be inordinately concerned with covering his own backside; but having no choice, he agreed to Lotz's terms and sold the plan to the BIT. He then designed and personally taught the inspector training classes which, like Nodulex advertising, stressed the fact that astronauts would owe their very lives to Nodulex quality.

Early Hi-Rel production yields revealed that Zwick's training had stuck — with a vengeance. Evidently thinking of those astronautical lives hanging in the balance, each inspector rejected far more units than he or she accepted. The operative criterion was rejection; too many acceptances might suggest that someone was not looking hard enough.

Appalled by the colossal rejection rate, Zwick decided that something was amiss with the operators on the Hi-Rel line. Rushing to meet a production deadline, he designed and taught another ten-hour course for Hi-Rel operators. Yields did improve somewhat.

What Zwick and Baker had not foreseen, however, was the enormous amount of time Hi-Rel devoured after it was up and running. The line worked in relatively small lots of twenty, but cells took forever with their work, determined to win the inspection game. Additional operator time, however, was nothing compared to delays inflicted by jittery inspectors who were more determined than ever to let no questionable units slip through.

What happened next was a nightmare. As Hi-Rel units moved past the inspection points, their numbers declined precipitously; and by the end of the process, they disappeared! Not one unit made it to the end of the line; all had either been scrapped or rejected for rework somewhere during manufacture. Truly alarmed, Zwick increased the lot size to fifty units. No change. It was six months before a trickle of product made it to packing.

That at least was a start, a leg up on better things. Proudly, Zwick showed the finished units to Lynn Snow, their design engineer. Pride turned to disbelief at Snow's response: "Hell, those things shouldn't be shipped. They've been handled so much that they'll fall apart when they're used. If they had any life it was used up in the inspection process."

No Hi-Rels.

And that, appallingly enough, was that. The project was ignominiously scrubbed. Zwick would never forget the dressing down he received from the normally affable Gerry Baker, who insisted that company credibility, Marketing's in particular, had been shafted by the whole fiasco. "What do I say to our customers?" Baker wanted to know. "They trusted us!" Zwick was damned if he knew.

Hi-Rel was embarrassing, all right, but Zwick continued to believe that Back On Track would save Nodulex. And he had the BIT's written support for that premise. Spring gave way to summer.

In August, Zwick was taken aback by the news that Big Lotz had handed his CEO's position to a stranger named Ann Moore. Just a week before the change of command was announced, Zwick had made an upbeat presentation to top management, winning Big Lotz's approval to expand Back On Track into the Service Division. He decided to hold back on that effort until Moore was aboard and understood the importance of his program. When, shortly after her arrival, Moore summoned key managers for a conference on quality performance, Zwick had enough improvement data on hand to raise any newcomer's consciousness.

Except that Moore did not become a believer. How could she, when neither Zwick nor anyone else at the conference could get a word in edge-wise? In truth, that entire meeting went badly. Being an old-fashioned guy at heart (and a guy who never read *Philadelphia Magazine*), Zwick was startled by the new CEO's smart suit, high heels, and short haircut, and was further nonplussed by her overabundant nervous energy. Was that called charisma? He wasn't sure, despite her title, how seriously to take such a person, and he wasn't alone in his reaction. The tension in the room was palpable. Moore did almost all the talking.

Moore was anxious about quality matters, but she used the terms "quality" and "competitiveness" interchangeably in her sweeping general-izations, bashing Nodulex's "baseline" performance figures with a blue-sky set of her own called "entitlement." To judge by the numbers she threw around, her concept of entitlement was a 20 percent improvement in sales and a 50 percent reduction in inventory! Profit? Moore expected to take Nodulex from none to "ten or fifteen million" within two years! Meanwhile, she stipulated, "costs will come way down and quality will skyrocket. We'll do this without adding resources."

As she made her skyrocket comment, Moore locked eyes with Zwick for the first time. Nodulex's quality czar knew it was now or never. He cut in: "Excuse me, but Back On Track will require an infusion of money if it is to proceed. We're getting results, and I'd hate to see..."

"I can see I'm going too fast and generalizing too much," said Moore, interrupting his interruption. "Tell you what. Next week, I'll meet with each of you one-on-one. I'm sure I can make a better case for my ideas if we get more specific. Meanwhile, please don't be misled by first impres-sions. You'll each be hearing from me in a few days." The Headlight that followed signaled a sudden end of the meeting. It was but moments later when Moore asked Zwick to be in her office first thing Monday morning, thus deep-sixing Zwick's vacation.

First thing Monday morning, with a fresh haircut and two copies of Back On Track objectives still warm from the photocopier, Zwick stood in Moore's office, waiting for the CEO's arrival. He felt exactly the way he had on his first day of Sunday School. Before long, Moore entered, flashed The Headlight and motioned him toward a barn-red suede sofa while she arranged herself behind her desk. Unlike other bigwigs Zwick had faced, Moore gave him her immediate attention, ignoring the accumulated message slips and mail lying atop her antique desk.

What followed took a different tack from Friday. For starters, Moore asked Zwick to share his assembled information with her, a move which put the quality czar at ease and unleashed his enthusiasm for the progress he had made. Zwick was especially proud of his new inspection and data system which, he assured Moore, would yield long-term benefits. He finished with the assurance that "our quality is going up — permanently — which will have a strategic effect on our competitiveness."

Having heard him out without commenting, Moore now sat back in her desk chair and fixed her gaze upon the opposite wall. After a moment she pulled some handwritten notes from a desk drawer, glanced at them, and spoke.

"I don't know how to break the news to you gently," she began, "but Back On Track is bad for this company. Quality is improving for the wrong reasons. And it's costing us more than we can afford."

Zwick was speechless — almost. He could see the orange hairs on the backs of his hands standing straight up. Could she? Never a yes man, he blurted out the maxim that quality pays for itself. "Furthermore," he added, "there is no substitute for it. If Nodulex would commit more resources to licking quality glitches, you'd see faster results — and increased sales."

"Hear me out, Zwick," replied Moore. "I admire your enthusiasm for the program. I've read the quality consultant's report. I'm aware that Back On Track started with a bang and that people believe it is important, at least for the moment. Having done my homework over the weekend, I'm also prepared to get down to cases. Tell me why you're personally so sold on it."

Zwick felt a single, tickling drop of perspiration roll down the groove of his back, but for the first time since Friday, he felt his confidence returning. Why mince words? "I'm sold because I'm getting results — quality results. The team's inspectors are sharp. They've prevented literally thousands — I have the exact breakdowns — of faulty modules from going out the door. Rejects by customers have declined almost 60 percent. Now, we're standardizing defect criteria..."

"Excuse me just a minute," Moore interjected. "Let's talk about those inspections. Are you saying your team inspectors are more effective than before Back On Track?"

"Absolutely. Now that they're quality people, not line people, they're more objective. Before Back On Track, they were accountable to line supervisors, and you know what that meant."

"It meant that defects were overlooked or fudged?"

"Right. But those days are over."

"So what happens to the increased number of defects your team uncovers?"

"We don't ship them. We reject them, and they're reworked or scrapped, depending on the problem." She's getting it, thought Zwick.

Moore scribbled a few lines on a pad, put down her gold ballpoint, and spread her fingertips on the desktop. Zwick hated red nail polish. "Because of those inspections, cycle times are getting longer," said Moore. She stared at Zwick, eyebrows raised meaningfully, then continued. "It takes longer than ever to ship some orders because of the time involved in rework. I saw exactly the same thing with Briktek's cycle times.

"But let me change the subject for a minute. Zwick, are you aware that lot sizes are increasing on the manufacturing line?"

"No," replied Zwick, "that's not my area of concern."

The Headlight flashed. "Not your area of *responsibility*, perhaps, but you should treat it as an area of concern, because the consultant report listed inventory reduction as one of Back On Track's fringe benefits. The larger lot sizes are swelling inventory, not shrinking it."

"What I meant," said Zwick, "was that there's no quality connection to the growing inventory because we rework defective units for shipment. I can't account for the larger lot sizes."

"I can. It is your fanatical inspection system. Manufacturing people have learned that there's safety in numbers. The larger the lot size, the more units will escape rejection. In other words, your inspectors are driving lot sizes up!

"Zwick, I'm a bean counter by training, so the first thing I checked about Back On Track was the way the program is measured — what you call the cost of unquality. Your measurements don't begin to show what the program is actually costing us. For example, last week we lost another Briktek order because our cycle time has gotten longer, not shorter. Know what made it longer? Elaborate inspection. Losing that order is the true cost of unquality. Meanwhile, I see a larger, costlier inspection staff, more rework, more scrap, and more inventory, all of which should be shrinking as quality improves.

"As far as I can see — and bear in mind that as CEO I have to take a bird's eye view — Back On Track is achieving higher quality at ruinous cost. I won't even go into the matter of Hi-Rel because it seems to have been a one-time thing, albeit an incredibly expensive one-time thing. Anyway, funding Back On Track increased our overhead dramatically. And if I recall Friday's meeting clearly, you intend to ask for more resources, resources we simply haven't got.

"Because Back On Track has lengthened our already unacceptable cycle times, we'll lose business no matter how well our stuff works. We have more cash than ever tied up in inventory — cash we must liberate to survive. Meanwhile, the company cut prices to increase sales, but because of long cycle times, those sales haven't materialized.

"All things considered, if module quality gets much better, we may be out of business!"

Now Zwick had his back up. Was Moore playing a mind game? "All this talk of costs and measurements is making us lose sight of the goal," he said. "Take the quality cells, for instance." Moore's nod indicated that she was familiar with the cells, so Zwick pushed on. "I was amazed, as I think you would be, by how many creative programs those cells have generated. They literally involve everyone in quality-mindedness and quality activities."

Moore perked up. "How many creative programs, roughly speaking?" she asked.

"Well, we've got thirty-six cells with one action in process per cell right now. But that's just scratching the surface. At least three hundred and fifty quality improvement proposals have been submitted."

"How long does it take to get a proposal approved and accomplished?"

"Ummm... it varies. The cells don't meet as often as they should because time is hard to come by. And it takes more time to prioritize their proposals. Completion dates range from three to twelve months — say six months on average. I figure we'll complete about six a month once we really get going."

"Good heavens! At that rate, it'll take five years to complete those three hundred and fifty actions in process! Back On Track doesn't *have* five years to complete its task. Unless things change drastically, Nodulex doesn't have five years, period." Just an hour earlier, Zwick was upset because he might not have a summer vacation. Now it hit him that he might not have a job.

Apparently reading his mind, Moore took a conciliatory tack: "Relax, Zwick. Nobody's questioning your dedication or threatening your position. There's plenty of work to do to make Nodulex quality the best in the industry. We can do it. Notice I said we. But I want a *total* approach to Nodulex quality.

"Back on Track is a spot fix, not a total approach. As such, it is counterproductive to company-wide competitiveness and quality alike. It's founded on the assumption that because quality is a prerequisite for competitiveness, products must be analyzed, inspected and reworked so that defects disappear. That doesn't work for long.

"Now don't get me wrong. A zero-defect objective is laudable in any company — essential, actually. But attacking defect rates is the wrong way to improve quality. It takes too long, it costs too much, and it doesn't eliminate the root causes of uncompetitive quality.

"There are two things wrong with this program. In the first place, it's a *program*, and it's perceived as such. When I talked to one old-timer last week about Back On Track, he told me he had been through 'program after program' at Nodulex and was willing to cooperate with this one if that's what management wanted. Think about that for a minute. So long as Nodulexers see Back On Track as a temporary cross they must bear to restore competitiveness, your results won't last. So long as Nodulexers see quality as the property of some special squad, they'll mentally pass the buck. They may clap and cheer for the cause — who wouldn't? — but they won't make it a permanent part of their work life.

"Quality cannot be a program. It must be an everyday way of life. Which brings me to my second point. Back On Track is steaming down the wrong track. To have first-rate, competitive quality, Nodulex must become more responsive to customers. Right now, Nodulex *isn't* responsive because our cycle times are too long. Processes with unacceptably long cycle times — baseline cycle times — are out of order, which prevents meaningful improvement. Nodulex needs to simplify those processes, getting rid of extraneous steps and barriers that complicate work and promote slip-ups. When that's done, quality will be better because the opportunities for slip-ups will be fewer.

"I'll put it to you this way, Zwick: Long cycle times are a sign of a company with quality problems. *Longer* cycle times — and that's what we've got here since Back On Track started — are a sign that overall quality is getting worse. To improve quality, we must eliminate the barriers to short cycle time. Your elaborate inspections are one of those barriers."

By now, a steady column of droplets was parading down Zwick's back, and he was in total confusion. Did it show? The new CEO was beginning to sound like a broken record on the subject of cycle time, which was apparently her cure-all for any problem. What was he supposed to say? That eliminating inspection steps sounded plumb crazy to him? That the logical way to improve quality was to take more care, not less? He decided to try one last appeal: "Do I understand correctly? Are you saying we don't need a quality program?"

Moore's propensity to talk in italics went into high gear: "I'm saying that a quality *program* is a symptom of a disorderly *culture*. No; we don't need a quality *program*. We need a quality *system*. No, we don't need Back On Track. At best, Back On Track squeezes incremental quality gains out of baseline processes instead of attacking the faulty processes themselves. Because of it, we take longer and longer to respond to customers. To a customer, responsiveness is a component of quality. Every gain we make through defect reduction is more than offset by our loss of responsiveness. Things have got to change.

"Back On Track is canceled, retroactive to Friday. Henceforth, our main thrust will be to attack our faulty processes, slimming them down — in Modules, Services, Marketing, you name it. *I want lean processes!*

"Now let's come back to your situation for a minute. Last Friday's meeting taught me that I can't accomplish this task alone. How about giving me some support? You've fought hard for quality-mindedness in this company. Hold on to that attitude. We are not abandoning quality by killing Back On Track. Just the opposite, in fact. I'll need some inside help, someone I can work with closely, someone I can count on. If you're really serious about quality, you'll take that slot. Keep your quality manager title. I promise you we'll overturn some major barriers around here and get results you'll be proud of. Are you game?"

Inasmuch as the occupational limb had just been sawed out from under him, Zwick was ready to break his free-fall as quickly as possible.

"I'm game," he said.

Game for what? Pacing the parking lot during lunchtime, former Quality Czar Hirtle Zwicker remembered the Back On Track bumper sticker on his Bronco and, when he was sure nobody was watching, peeled it off with his penknife. That evening, alone in his silent, stuffy house, ensconced in his overstuffed Barcalounger, he poured himself a double Dewar's straight up and plopped a videocassette of last year's summer vacation into the VCR. The picture was a blur; his mind kept wandering.

Game for what?

COMMENTARY

Chapter Two

My heart goes out to Zwick. No sooner had he convinced himself that Back On Track could turn Nodulex around than his program was stopped cold. The abrupt turn of events must have been hard to swallow, especially when perpetrated by a new CEO, an outsider necessarily unversed in Nodulex culture. Zwick, however, was in for a rude awakening sooner or later because, like about 80 percent of corporate quality programs, Back On Track was fatally flawed.

From the start, Nodulex was overinspired. The excitement of that initial kickoff generated high expectations without providing clear direction or a satisfactory way of measuring results. The program also generated a great deal of paperwork. With so many teams proposing so many actions and requesting so many new resources, Back On Track would become a breeding ground of frustration and confusion.

The Hi-Rel experiment at least took a stab at establishing a lead steer in the product line, but again, the approach was doomed. By attempting to catch defects through elaborate inspection, Hi-Rel mistook inspection for quality and activity for results.

Ann Moore's energetic manner was not enough at first to offset her lack of command experience and the apparent gender prejudice of her new subordinates. Although her one-on-one meeting with Zwick produced no instant rapport, it did establish who was boss and why Nodulex's quality program was an illusion. Like many time-based managers, Moore was adept at spotting generic process and cultural barriers that complicate work and lengthen cycle time. That skill, along with her outside perspective, enabled her to see that Back On Track, however well-intentioned, was counterproductive to both quality and competitiveness.

With Back On Track, Zwick had been doing the wrong things for the right reasons. By agreeing to work with Moore despite his misgivings, he would at least be doing the right thing for the wrong reasons.

Quality Programs as Barriers

Quality improvement programs have a way of becoming barriers to their own stated objective because their emotional quotient distracts people from taking appropriate action. Recently, I witnessed a typical instance of that sort at a large aerospace company. Fired with zeal for its newly adopted quality mindset, that company's management trained its work force in quality management principles and authorized the establishment of "action teams" to identify and eradicate quality glitches wherever they might be. A hurricane was unleashed: teams popped up in all places and at all levels, each one attacking a particular part of the overall business process. How many teams? No one knew. Bottom-line results? Aside from the cost of training and team activity, none could be measured even after a year of activity. Improvement in the company's competitive position? None could be detected. Very discouraging.

Or consider the following example, passed on to me by a colleague who understandably wishes to remain anonymous. This one makes Back On Track seem positively inspired. A manufacturer of forklift trucks found itself with quality problems after moving its assembly operations to the Orient. Under the new procedure, truck kits were shipped overseas, assembled, and returned to the home factory for final preparation such as the attachment of wheels and special options.

Inevitably, the overseas strategy complicated the business process and lengthened cycle time. Quality slipped so badly that it was necessary to establish a stateside modification-and-repair center to bring products up to standard before shipping. More steps; longer cycle times. "One day," my friend told me, "the president decided the company needed to add on or overlay a *Quality Program*. Accordingly, the company's quality guru acquired a set of sixteen video tapes by the famous Dr. Joseph Juran, to be viewed as a group by the president and all vice presidents. Since everyone's calendar was full, weekly tape viewings were scheduled for 7:00 a.m. over a period of sixteen weeks.

"The program took off at a snail's pace as top management waded through this sensitivity training in quality improvement. Each viewing was preceded by guru inspiration and followed by warm group discussion. The new religion was, of course, earnestly professed by one and all during these weekly sacraments, replete with obligatory testimonials. The converts competitively recited gratifying results purportedly achieved in each functional area as a result of the newly internalized quality fix.

"One morning, after a dozen or so tapes had been viewed, the vice president of operations was compelled to confess that, in a slight backsliding, a new forklift truck had been shipped without wheels! Apparently no one had noticed until the dealer called the company to complain. The poor operations VP had to endure ridicule as his peers speculated on how he would creatively explain to the dealers that quality really had gotten better....

"As a discrete 'program,' the new, feel-good quality cram course, long on sloganeering and exhortation, had completely failed to address the underlying causes of poor quality: complicated business processes and interminable cycle times with no effective [learning] feedback."

Defect Reduction as a Barrier

Returning to Nodulex, Back On Track's goal of achieving the lowest defect rate in the industry was desirable in itself. But by adding inspection steps to the manufacturing line, Back On Track was lengthening cycle times, making Nodulex slower than ever in responding to customer orders. Here was a cultural blind spot — a barrier to competitive performance — that might have proven fatal.

Aside from the damage it would do to Nodulex's flagging business, the inspection route indicated a fundamental misunderstanding about what constitutes quality. Fundamentally, good quality occurs when customers are satisfied. Lengthening cycle times would inevitably alienate the company's already exasperated clients, making the defect rate altogether irrelevant.

Back On Track was further undermining quality in subtle ways. For example, it was teaching bad habits. Zwick's inspection team, no longer accountable to manufacturing, naturally became more zealous and exacting. Familiar with the ins and outs of manufacturing, inspectors knew what to look for in order to nab more faulty units than before. On the line, manufacturing people quickly learned how to play the inspection game, devoting more and more effort to fooling their former peers. Devising ways to evade inspection snafus was not the same thing as producing better modules; meanwhile, it lengthened cycle time and reduced the number of opportunities to improve quality by using the lessons of experience, a process I call Cycles of Learning. (Cycles of Learning will be discussed at length in Chapter five's commentary.) Between the inspectors' methods and the pressure to optimize lot acceptance, lot sizes went up and so did cycle time.

It is of course important that inspection criteria be closely matched to customers' needs. Using any other set of measurements, inspectors are apt to flag "substandard" items that would perform acceptably in practical use. Just what constituted a defective module anyway? Zwick's attempt to develop defect criteria via forms and photographs was another well-intentioned tactic that looked better than it worked because it complicated the task of inspectors, tying them up with paperwork and debate about what was or was not a defect. Time, Nodulex's most precious commodity, was lost in this process.

As painful as the news must have been to Zwick, Ann Moore's assessment of Back On Track was right on target. Quality efforts are too often overlays on a process, not integral to it. Good intentions notwithstanding, Back On Track had segregated itself from the manufacturing system at Nodulex and thus had undermined the principle that quality was everybody's business. Worse, it was treating the symptoms of the faulty manufacturing process, not its root causes.

Back On Track's most egregious oversight was failing to recognize the direct, root-cause connection between short cycle times and high quality. Speed is often perceived as the enemy of quality, whereas the opposite is almost always the case. Because he equated meticulous, attentive care with defect reduction, Zwick assumed that more inspections would ensure better quality. Moore's repeated insistence that quality was achievable only through shortened, simplified processes went against his grain.

Moore was convinced that removing unnecessary hurdles in the manufacturing process would improve quality by reducing the opportunities for things to go wrong. And, as cycle time came down, there would be more opportunities to learn from experience — Cycles of Learning — which would accelerate the refinement of defect-free manufacturing.

Quality Programs as Bottomless Pits

As with most quality improvement programs, Back On Track's natural tendency was to grow. An incremental reduction in defects implied that further improvement could be gained by adding more quality people, or more data tracking, or more teams, or more money. Accordingly, the cost of quality was going up. The real goal of a quality organization should be to work itself out of a job, not the opposite. Few quality teams endeavor to put themselves out of business. When people are hired to find defects they will do so.

The Need for Meaningful Measurements

Back On Track's way of measuring itself was meaningless in any real-world context. Not only had Zwick missed the importance of customer satisfaction as a measurement of quality, but he regarded the hundreds of uncompletable activities spawned by his quality cells as quantitative proof that his program was working!

Zwick was not alone in his attitude about quality improvement at Nodulex. He obviously represented a consensus of top management, not to mention the consultant who had drafted the plan. Such consensus constituted an enormous cultural barrier to effective performance. In a word, it presumed that quality drives a business and, therefore, actions taken on behalf of quality add value to a business. Not so.

Do Quality Programs Add Value?

Cultural blindness permitted another layer of process barriers to be added to the business task. Not one of Back On Track's intensified inspections, additional resources, new people, and increased paperwork added a dime's worth of value to the manufacturing process. Unless the trend were reversed, all would be nails in the Nodulex coffin. Looked at in terms of the Three R's of competitiveness — Responsiveness, Results Acceleration, and Resource Effectiveness — Back On Track was an across-the-board failure from the moment of its inception.

Zwick's encounter with Moore left him with his job intact but with his confidence so shaken that he had agreed to assist Moore's time-based quality approach, whatever that was. If, as Moore correctly insisted, first-rate quality could occur only where process cycle times were as low as possible, Nodulex was in for a real shakeup. Before long, Zwick would be hearing Moore's dictum that "Total Cycle Time is *the* driver of improved quality" in his sleep.

Chapter Three

Measuring The Competitive Quality Gap

Was she game? That question nagged Ann Moore through the month of August, when each day made clearer the magnitude of the Nodulex crisis. Not that she lacked the courage of her convictions; but knowing what needed to be done and doing it properly were two different things. Her flawless grasp of the theory of competitive quality was, she knew, not matched by practical experience in implementing those ideas. Everyone else at Nodulex probably knew it too. Her recent contacts with management did little to improve her confidence.

Then there was the matter of temperament. Was it partly anxiety about her lack of executive experience, she wondered, that made her come on too strong, bowling over subordinates with an agitated verbal barrage that got in the way of her message? Was she overcompensating for the fact that her expertise in the Wonderful World of Modules was zilch? Was she venting frustration at her hidebound managers' unmistakable male condescension? All of the above?

Ironically, these and other professional misgivings overwhelmed her not on work days but on weekends, which she customarily spent exploring the Pennsylvania Dutch country west of Philadelphia in search of folk art for her immense collection. She made these forays alone, usually dressed in jeans, a Stanford sweatshirt, and designer sunglasses. If a Nodulexer had crossed her path at such times, she would have gone unrecognized.

Moore's weekend sojourns were not escapes. Somehow, the solitary pleasure of her rovings lowered her mental guard, allowing the week's job pressures to reassert themselves with surprising power, speaking to her instinctual rather than her practical side. So it was that far from her office, Moore often had flashes of insight about how to deal with professional problems.

A twice-divorced, transplanted Californian who came east to make a fresh start at Briktek, she had never gotten over her initial delight that treasures worthy of a museum could be found in the antique shops and flea markets of rural Pennsylvania. That was what drew her to the countryside every chance she got. Her favorite possession was a wooden horse weathervane she had spotted atop a Cumberland County barn ten years ago and bought on the spot from an amazed farmer. That purchase began a collection of sculptural figures and trade signs that grew and improved as Moore shot up the corporate ladder to affluence. By the time she moved to Nodulex, part of her collection was on loan to the Museum of American Folk Art in New York and she had published an article on the subject in *Americana Magazine.*

Compulsively protective of her privacy, Moore lived quietly in a restored eighteenth-century brick townhouse in Society Hill. She seldom entertained; but on such occasions, unsuspecting guests were invariably delighted by her houseful of artfully placed vanes, cigar store figures, ship figureheads, and carousel animals. "These are my family," she would say with a shrug and a smile, gesturing to her accumulated treasures and revealing more about herself than she realized. Indeed, she drew both pleasure and strength from the silent, companionable presence of her "family." If anyone suspected that Moore's collecting was a substitute for meaningful human contact, the matter was never broached. Although she was well paid both at Briktek and Nodulex, Moore's collecting and the mortgage on her townhouse left her little disposable income at the end of each month, a fact which, in view of her track record, did not trouble her.

But something — or some things — certainly were troubling her five days after meeting with Zwick. Cruising back roads near Marietta, Pennsylvania, Moore felt the bad vibes of her new responsibility creep up and envelop her in a wave of anxiety. She did not fight back. Years of coping with personal setbacks and executive pressure had taught her to identify the components of her distress, bring her energy to bear on the ones

48

she could control, and waste no time on those she could not. By such means she was usually able to whittle her anxiety down to a tolerable level.

She began this process, as always, by reminding herself that her jitters were partly attributable to hard-wired habit she had acquired as a child. Her parents, professors of history and art at a small California college, had bent the twig relentlessly toward the work ethic, insisting on overachievement as a prerequisite for their approval. They had also trained her in their own image, fully anticipating for her a career in the arts or the social sciences or both. By the age of five, Ann had built up a lifetime supply of of fretful perfectionism, enough to ensure that she would achieve major anxiety and major results in any undertaking. College provided her with a vehicle to go her own way. Showing an aptitude for math and technical subjects, Moore elected a career course different from the one her parents had so carefully prepared for her. Feeling betrayed, they had never forgiven her for that act of independence. By unspoken agreement, parents and daughter saw each other only on rare occasions.

Moore's hardwired perfectionism proved crucial to her rapid professional advancement and the undermining of her two marriages. She was, she knew, a loner with no means of support save her own hardnosed intellect. Intellectually, Moore understood and accepted the consequences of such things. But when, as at Nodulex, a new, critical challenge presented itself, she had to work diligently to fight down generalized panic.

As she drove through the picturesque Pennsylvania countryside, she reconsidered her power position at Nodulex and reminded herself that it was far stronger than it looked. During her negotiations with the Nodulex board, her primary attraction was a proven ability to improve performance using Total Cycle Time techniques. All board members from Big Lotz down understood that fixing the company required a comprehensive change of corporate culture, no less; her contract said so in writing. In the event of a showdown, then, she would prevail.

Could she avoid a showdown? Initial meetings with entrenched managers had been inauspicious and, with the exception of Hirtle Zwicker, downright awkward. No question: As an outsider she had a fresh slant on the tangled processes and cultural blindness at Nodulex, but unless she proceeded with care and diplomacy, she could jeopardize the company's future despite the soundness of her ideas. Trouble was, there might not be time enough to practice diplomacy.

During her undergraduate years at Stanford, Moore had taken a

European history course called "The Age of Reason," in which she was struck by the failure of the period's progressive monarchs to accomplish their intended reforms. Despite absolute power and the best of intentions, those rulers had been defeated by the sheer weight of bureaucratic and cultural inertia, and, in the end, they achieved pathetically few of their objectives. Today, wheeling her van along the byways of Lebanon County, Moore saw herself in a similar light. She had probably underestimated the power of baseline inertia at Nodulex.

Her undergraduate years now seemed a century ago; so, for that matter, did her graduate work at Stanford's Sloan Business School. It was there, during a couple of guest lectures, that she had first encountered cycle time thinking. Those lectures were ahead of their time but she'd never forgotten their message. Who was that lecturer who'd put a bee in her bonnet back then? Earl... what was it... Gossamer? No... Gomersall!

Something clicked in Moore's mind: That name, she suddenly realized, appeared on two *Harvard Business Review* articles she had lately Xeroxed. There couldn't be more than one cycle-time guru named Gomersall. Another click: One Gomersall was all she needed at Nodulex.

Moore had lost track of where she had been steering her van. She now found herself entering a small village altogether new to her. Without missing a turn, she managed to find the central square, parked, entered the town library ("Open Saturday 10 to 4") and made a beeline for the reference section. The library copy of *Who's Who* was not the latest, but.... There he was, on page 1236: "Gomersall, Earl Raymond, consultant...." Below that citation was a fat chronology of high-level, high-tech corporate positions, publications, and patents. And there, at the bottom of the biographical sketch, was his home address. Click!

At times like this, Moore instinctually practiced what she preached about short cycle time. Rushing from the library, she found a phone booth next to a corner Arco station, dialed Information for suburban Chicago and, following that, rang Gomersall's home number. Was this crazy? Before she could have second thoughts, Gomersall answered.

Moore introduced herself. "Are you still a consultant, as it says in *Who's Who*?" she asked.

The voice at the other end was understandably cool. "I call myself a resultant," was the reply. "In my specialty, 'consulting' carries a here-today-gone-tomorrow stigma. I sell solutions tied to results, not programs. Does your company need to improve its results?"

Not wanting to quibble about terminology, Moore plunged into a quick, adrenalized reprise of her predicament. Her use of cycle-time jargon quickly broke the ice. After a rapid rundown of Nodulex's baseline condition and her estimate of its entitlement prospects, she came to the point: "To answer your question, Nodulex damn well better improve its results. I need someone with instant credibility to help me get a precise estimate of Nodulex's entitlement, instill Cycles of Learning, and oversee some quick hole-plugging and pumping out. You, if possible. *Now*, if possible."

"What's wrong with *your* credibility?" asked Gomersall.

"Nothing. Everything. I understand Total Cycle Time because I had a full dose of it at Briktek." Gomersall interjected that he was familiar with Briktek. Moore continued: "I know what I'm talking about, but nobody else at Nodulex does. I'm impatient because more delay can kill this company. My impatience, however, garbles my message.

"That's not all. You may as well know, though I doubt it will surprise you, that some Nodulex oldtimers are completely thrown by having to deal with a female CEO who came in from left field. And it's throwing *me*. Mind you, I'm not afraid of a challenge, macho or otherwise. If Nodulex were nearer its entitlement, I'd take things in stride and manage us out of the woods. But the woods are very deep around here, and I don't have time...."

"I get it. Fax me a profile of the situation today and I'll call you tonight." Moore and Gomersall exchanged numbers and rung off.

Moore could almost hear her heart pounding as she returned to her van (where was she, anyway?). Her appetite for antiquing had completely left her. At the first crossroads she headed south and eventually picked up the Pennsylvania Turnpike below Cornwall. Within two hours, she was back at her center city home. She faxed Gomersall the necessary particulars, showered, microwaved a Lean Cuisine and, when it was gone, sat down to wait. She could hear the voices of children playing in a pocket park nearby; otherwise, there was not a sound outside. For the first time, she noticed how spooky her unlit study looked filled with shadowy human and animal shapes. As the setting sun left the room in darkness, however, her eyes became accustomed to the gloom and the sinister shadows were again recognizable, even comforting. Then the phone rang.

"I'd like to help you," said Gomersall, skipping the preliminaries, "and right now I have some free time. From what I've seen, your estimate of the situation is on target. But I have to tell you I've had it with corporate politics — barriers that keep new ideas from getting institutionalized. You're facing a cultural stone wall at Nodulex. Getting the company to entitlement could be very tough, and keeping entitlement once you've made it could be even harder. But I'll come aboard if you're willing to take me on my terms."

"Which are?"

"Number one: I report to you. Number two: I spend my weekends at home. Three: After you reach entitlement, you'll touch base with me periodically to safeguard your gains. Four: If, together, we don't bring Nodulex to its entitled level of quality performance and profit, I'll waive my fee."

"You sound awfully confident on awfully short notice."

"Well, if you're as smart as you sound, that shouldn't surprise you. Anyway, it's the task that intrigues me, not the fee. I learned the hard way what you're finding out now: You can't be a prophet in your own company because you'll be branded as a trouble-making maverick, somebody who's fixing things that aren't broken."

"Exactly," replied Moore as the adrenaline cut in. "It happened just last week. My quality manager thought I was crazy for relating short cycle times to high quality. To him, quality takes time. I couldn't make him see the light."

"So it goes. Well, if *you* can't be a prophet in your own company, maybe I can. Another strike against you is that you're a *generalist*, not someone with a Ph.D. in modules. I'll bet that fact does you more harm than your age and sex put together." Moore was not at all sure this was so, but she let Gomersall continue. "A *generalist* is exactly what Nodulex needs right now, but that's a hard sell to specialists. Let me handle that; I've been there before. In fact, I'll fax you today a half-dozen corporate references — companies where I've delivered results. Check 'em out. If we make a deal, the results will be your vindication. *Our* vindication."

Moore loved people who spoke in italics. She gave Gomersall her fax number and, while they talked about working arrangements, her nearby machine spat out a list of companies at least four of which were larger and, she was certain, more competitive than Nodulex.

Click! "I'll read over the references you've sent and make a few phone calls," she said. "Unless they provide some bad surprises, we have a deal."

Although she had seen him lecture years before, Moore had retained no idea of what Gomersall looked like, so it took her a moment to identify the person already seated in her office first thing Monday morning. What she beheld was a blue-blazered, thick-set man of indeterminate age, hair combed in a fifties-style pompadour, fingering a large, black, mercifully unlit cigar and squinting menacingly at Zwick, who was providing a quality rundown on the company. Zwick had received a telephone summons from Moore the night before.

Zwick watched silently as Gomersall casually plopped his cigar in an antique slipware dish he had mistaken for an ash tray atop Moore's desk. Moore's knuckles grew white as her grip on the edge of her desk tightened, but she said nothing. "Nice place you got here," said Gomersall. Then the three sat down to strategize.

Moore let Zwick explain the company's quality situation in his own words, resisting the temptation to interfere. Probably just as well, she figured, Gomersall had heard this sort of thing many times. When Zwick had finished, Gomersall suggested, in light of the fact that Back On Track had started inside the Module Division, that he, Moore and Zwick do the same with their assessment. "We already have a picture of baseline," said Moore, "but my estimate of entitlement was pretty hasty."

"Okay," said Gomersall, "where do we start?"

"With Howie Lotz. He's the Module Division's VP."

Howard Lotz was a lifelong suburbanite and fitness fanatic whose permanent tennis tan emphasized his prime physical condition. Unless one noticed the half-dollar-sized bald spot and the dozens of tiny lines crisscrossing his sunburnt face, he looked ten years younger than he was.

Lotz possessed a unique set of credentials for his vice presidency: an MBA from the Wharton School and eleven years in his present position. He also possessed an ironic sense of humor which had come in handy because, as nephew of the company's late CEO and present board chairman, he had been in a perpetual spotlight at Nodulex. Before the company's profits went south, he was presumed to be the next chief executive.

Moore's sudden arrival had forced Lotz to reassess his professional position, and he was surprised by his own candor in doing so. Taking stock, he admitted to himself that he had worn his heir-apparent mantle uncomfortably. He was especially thin-skinned about the nickname Nodulexers used behind his back: "Little Lotz," although that moniker was intended only to differentiate him from his illustrious uncle. There were, he decided, two reasons for his touchiness. One was the fact that, connections notwithstanding, Howard Lotz was a well-trained, capable, manager who would be a credit to any company. The other was that the expectation of his rise to the very top originated with other people, not himself. Living with that expectation, he now realized, had been so burdensome that Ann Moore's arrival was a pleasant surprise. If worse came to worst, she, not he, would bear the stigma of sinking the family enterprise.

Family loyalties aside, what kept Howard Lotz at Nodulex? After thirteen sessions of psychological counseling and several all-night discussions with his wife Sandra, he concluded that he liked the work. His tasks were interesting, not overly taxing. He believed in Comfortability, which afforded him time for a private life. If he ever had to prove something, he was still young enough to find a similar or better spot elsewhere. Meanwhile, he owed it to himself, his family, and his employees to stick around until Nodulex was out of the woods.

Lotz was beginning to realize that getting out of the woods might be a long, unpleasant trek. Like every other senior manager, he had just gone one-on-one with Moore, which had added confusion to his characteristic impatience. He'd been surprised by the cancellation of Back On Track; but now, just days later, he was facing another curative approach: Total Cycle Time. Enough, already!

Lotz's reluctance to salute the cycle time flag was not prompted by any objection to its principles. He had immediately grasped the need for a sweeping approach to improvement. Obviously, Back On Track had been a scattershot, piecemeal approach that complicated his division's daily tasks and multiplied his own paperwork. Good riddance. He also had no problem with Moore's insistence that quality was a result of orderly processes, not vice versa. Lotz's bone of contention was that, in his opinion, the Module Division's processes were already orderly. When Nodulex had gone on its cost-cutting binge, his division had produced a careful self-study that corroborated his opinion. Under the circumstances, he was damned if he would take a dive so the new CEO could play with the processes.

All of this passed through Lotz's mind when he got word from Moore that someone named Gomersall was about to assess the Module Division's "entitlement potential." In reply to the announcement, he sent a fresh copy of the division's self-study to Moore's office covered by a memo that read "This should make clear that the Module Division already operates at its entitlement potential." Lotz, who was as quick as anyone to glom onto buzzwords, got a chuckle out of writing that memo.

He did not chuckle when the memo came back bearing Moore's initials under a one-word response: "Baloney." Uh-oh. Could this cycle-time thing possibly be getting out of control? To Lotz's mind, the last thing Modules needed was another intrusive "improvement program." He filed the baloney memo and waited for the next ominous development.

Word came following next day that Gomersall and Zwick — Zwick! — were launching their "independent entitlement assessment." The whole idea struck Lotz as bizarre, almost crackpot. Who the hell was this Gomersall? Probably a nobody who'd soon ride off into the sunset like all consultants. Whoever he was, he'd be in good company with Zwick who, since the Hi-Rel fiasco, was likewise a nobody. Meanwhile, Lotz had a division to run.

The assessment team had allowed itself one week to complete its survey. To quickly determine the Module Division's baseline-entitlement gap, Moore, Gomersall, and Zwick used a four-step approach. First, they gathered and scrutinized all of the division's available financial records. Then they conferred with staffers. Following that, they met with a horizontal cross-section of the division, from Lotz's office to the loading dock. Finally, they synthesized the division's baseline and entitlement figures from the data and personal interviews.

Zwick was inclined to be a bystander to the assessment procedure but Gomersall repeatedly drew him in. "Remember, Zwick," he said on day one as they walked to the Module Division's offices, "this exercise is an attempt to determine where to improve performance. In other words, we're searching for pockets of unquality that can be eliminated. One difference between this assessment and other quality approaches is the way we'll measure quality. We'll use four indicators." With that, Gomersall slipped Zwick an unlined sheet of paper bearing the following handwritten message:

MEASUREMENTS OF COMPETITIVE QUALITY

1. CYCLE TIME

2. FIRST-PASS YIELD

3. COST

4. INVENTORY LEVELS

"That's for your new file," said Gomersall. On good behavior and ready for anything at this point, Zwick had equipped himself with a new folder into which he tucked the memo.

Gomersall grunted, nodded, and rolled his unlit cigar from the left to the right side of his mouth. As the two strolled along a manufacturing line, he began an informal tutorial. Not once did he look directly at Zwick; instead, he squinted right and left at the line's noisy activity.

"Cycle time is the time that elapses between the beginning and completion of a discrete action," Gomersall began. "It is what drives improvement in every business. Here in manufacturing, it is computed by dividing the units of work-in-process inventory by the number of units completed in a given period. But cycle time is a vital measurement for *any* sector of a business, blue- or white-collar, engineering, finance, even sales and marketing. In nonmanufacturing situations it is simply the number of actions in process divided by their completion rate.

"Examine the actions in process within any given task and you'll almost always expose a number of steps that are considered valid but which add no value to the intended objective. When you eliminate those actions, your cycle time shortens and you hasten your intended results without quickening the pace of work or adding resources.

"Although every manager thinks his or her operation is unique, the same types of valueless procedures show up in process after process, business after business. That's why nonmodule types like Annie and I can improve competitiveness and quality inside Nodulex. We know those non-value-added process steps when we see them." Zwick smiled at the Annie reference. Ah, the human touch, he thought.

Gomersall continued. "As you saw on the sheet I gave you, the second vital quality measurement is first-pass yield. First-pass yield is simply the percentage of actions in a cycle that are completed right on the first attempt."

At long last, Zwick thought of something to say: "Howie Lotz has been measuring first-pass yield as long as I can remember."

"Okay," responded Gomersall. "Maybe I'm belaboring the obvious; maybe not. But most people compute first-pass yield incorrectly, with very unfortunate results. I'll bet you a jelly doughnut that the Module Division's yield estimates are way off the mark." Zwick was neither a betting man nor an argumentative one, but the pinched expression on his face suggested he had something to say. "Any comments?" Gomersall asked as the two made their way along another manufacturing line.

"Well, yes. I'd better point out that when it comes to measurements, Nodulex has a state-of-the-art system that's second to none. I mean, that system pours out reams of data."

"So what?" asked Gomersall.

"Come again?"

"I said, so what? Ann went over the system with me. I'd say that about 90 percent of the indices are in place to justify actions. Aside from that, they're not worthwhile. The company measures miles in millimeters and carries work standards to five decimal points. The truth is that Nodulex is spilling more money on accuracy and precision measurements than the results are worth.

"Consider first-pass yield for a moment. A jelly doughnut says this division hasn't a clue about its true first-pass yield despite all the data tracking."

Zwick rose to the defense of his company: "We have several bar-coded data collection stations that give us real-time information on how many units are completed at each set-up. This helps us control set-ups and labor."

"Let's check it out," said Gomersall. "In reducing cycle time, it's crucial to know how much work in process you have at every station. For example, what about this station right here?"

"We don't know what the WIP is, exactly," responded Zwick, "but we do know the hours scheduled for this work center."

"At what capacity?"

"Well, we're not sure."

"How many units went into this operation? How many are still there? And, of the ones that went in, how many good ones came out? What happened to the difference?"

"I couldn't tell you without combining a lot of station reports and doing some hand calculation. But the control system simulates our WIP in dollars for every work center every month."

"Do you manufacture modules or dollars?"

"Modules, of course!"

"Okay, how many modules failed to make it through the first time or didn't make it through at all?"

"We don't know. The foreman is supposed to make out a defective material report when time permits, but tracking it back to a machine or an individual operator would be next to impossible."

"What you're saying, Zwick, is that you have data on everything except what you need to run this business properly. In other words, you don't know and can't calculate your first-pass yield with the data you do have."

"I guess not."

"Did it ever occur to you or the manufacturing boys that if you measured your operations on first-pass yield and WIP — and used the feedback from those data to generate learning — none of the other measurements would be necessary?"

This took a moment to sink in. Zwick did not look pleased by the revelation. "Nope," he said. "I have to admit it never occurred to me. Or to the manufacturing boys, as you call them, so far as I know."

As Gomersall and Zwick continued their stroll, the tutorial proceeded. "There's a third important measurement of quality: what the process costs. Consider the non-value-added steps that clutter each and every process in a company like this one. Unnecessary actions that complicate manufacturing, administration, design, sales, marketing, you name it. In addition to the fact that they do nothing to drive competitiveness or good quality, each of those steps costs something. A process that involves only value-adding steps will have lower labor content, lower inventory carrying cost, and will require less space and equipment to operate. Its costs will therefore be significantly lower than those of a similar operation running at baseline. That's why cost is an important measurement of quality."

Zwick's brain was reaching information overload, but Gomersall was obviously determined to finish his four-point lecture on quality indices. He pressed on.

"The fourth measurement, inventory level, is self-explanatory. Suffice it to say that by the rules of Total Cycle Time, inventory levels must be minimal. Now, inasmuch as Nodulex is financially strapped, Ann and I went over the inventory figures first thing, hoping to free up some immediate cash. We were aghast. The inventory situation throughout the company is, in a word, horrendous.

"Get this: the Module Division is shelling out $4.5 million annually in inventory carrying costs. That's the equivalent of $22 million in sales if the company were at its old profit margin levels. Horrendous! Nodulex is wallowing in inventory that'll be flushed forever as the company moves up to entitlement. Here are the numbers for your file." Gomersall handed Zwick another sheet which read

INVENTORY FIGURES, MODULE DIVISION

	BASELINE	ENTITLEMENT
	(MILLIONS OF DOLLARS)	
Raw Material	4	3
Work-in-process	6	2
Finished Goods	8	4
Potential Cash Savings	9	
Carrying Cost Savings (25%)	2.2	

"Look at the cash saved by running a quality operation," said Gomersall. "Look at the improvement potential if we cut the amount of work in process. Speed from low cycle times and accuracy from high first-pass yields will reduce the levels of WIP and finished goods on hand. In addition, predictable schedules will reduce the necessary amount of raw material inventory. Now there's a slant on quality anyone can appreciate."

Zwick had to admit he could appreciate results like that; but they remained to be seen. Meanwhile, he wondered, how would Howie Lotz greet the news that his inventory was "horrendous?" Inventory was crucial when customers needed modules in a hurry.

Getting down to business, Gomersall assured Zwick that he intended to cut all cycle times in the division . The obvious place to start, though, was the manufacturing line. To determine the line's work-in-process cycle time, he and Zwick totaled the actions in progress on the line (the total WIP inventory) and divided that figure by the throughput rate to finished goods. That gave them a baseline figure: an average of three weeks.

To determine entitlement, they used existing data to calculate how long it would take to produce one module from start to finish straight through the line, without any of the usual waits, interruptions, rework or shift delays. The resulting figure provided a theoretical cycle time: an eye-popping four hours. "The division's entitlement lies somewhere between four hours and three weeks," said Gomersall.

"Hold it," said Zwick. "This theoretical figure is crazy in practical terms. Entitlement must be closer to three weeks than to four hours."

"That's what everybody thinks at first," said Gomersall, "because they underestimate how much time and effort are expended on unnecessary steps and barriers. As a rule, entitlement turns out to be two or three times theoretical, say twelve hours in this case. Now think what it would mean for customer satisfaction if the division could deliver orders in a matter of days, not weeks. By the way, what *would* it mean?"

"It would mean that we could outmaneuver our fastest competitor. It would mean that Briktek would love us — so long as we were shipping top-notch stuff. But if we start cutting corners, eliminating steps, our product quality will suffer. There's no benefit in that."

"Quality won't suffer, Zwick, because the steps we'll eliminate add no value. They're either irrelevant to quality or they're barriers to quality. We're going to unclutter the process, not cut corners. Trust me on this for the moment."

The following day, for a sanity check on his theoretical figure, Gomersall asked Lotz for any records of instances when the division had outperformed itself. Although he was still keeping a polite distance from the assessment, Lotz proudly produced several shining examples in which emergency orders were pulled through the line in a matter of days.

Gomersall shared this news with Moore; who was delighted. She then memoed Lotz her congratulations, adding the observation that entitlement performance often approximated the absolute best performance at baseline, in this case a few days. "See what's possible?" she concluded. She gave a copy of the memo to Zwick ("For your file!"), adding that Lotz should be included in the first-pass yield assessment.

Under the old regime, Zwick's quality crew had been consulted only when things went wrong, so he too was surprised by the Module Division's best-case histories. In spite of himself, he was getting curious about what was possible on an everyday basis. As long as he could remember, Nodulexers had viewed improvement as an incremental increase over the status quo. Perhaps it made sense to chuck all preconceptions about "effective performance" and start thinking about absolute best.

Although he was beginning to accept a broader definition of quality, Zwick had by no means discarded his own previous criteria. Neither, he thought, had Howie Lotz.

For some time, Nodulex quality, once the industry standard, had been matched by nimbler competitors; yet by its own measurements, Module Division quality was still impressive. Deliveries were consistently 98 percent to committed schedule thanks to the high finished goods inventory and the comfortably long delivery times the company quoted to customers. The fact that Nodulex, not its customers, scheduled the deliveries probably explained why some customers were dissatisfied with the company's near-perfect adherence to schedule.

The assessment team met with Lotz and his manufacturing staff to discuss first-pass yield. Moore saw to it that the two other VPs, Marketing's Gerry Baker, and Service's Colin West, also attended. Her announced intention was to give Marketing and Service a look at what was afoot in manufacturing so that they could sense the shape of things to come in their own bailiwicks. It was the first time since her rocky introductory session that Moore had had all her VPs in one place.

Not surprisingly, the meeting took the form of another tutorial. Moore began by stressing that first-pass yield was a crucial indicator of quality, a measurement that could be applied to any work cycle, not merely manufacturing. Quickly climbing on the bandwagon, Baker expressed satisfaction with the company's 99 percent first-pass yield in deliveries to schedule. Moore wasn't buying. She pointed out that "inasmuch as Nodulex does its own scheduling, the yield figure for delivery is a self-serving quality index." Nice try, Gerry, thought Zwick.

Lotz agreed with Moore: "Our high percentage of on-time delivery would be valid only if customers dictated the schedule. But our yield in manufacturing is almost as high: 95 percent. That's quality by anybody's standard."

At this point, Gomersall entered the discussion. "How do you measure first-pass yield?" he asked.

"Same as everyone," replied Lotz. "We divide output by input with adjustments for inventory change." Zwick noticed simultaneous grins crossing the features of Moore and Gomersall. After a few more questions, Gomersall determined that the 95 percent figure included a substantial amount of rework done on uncompleted products before they reached the end of the manufacturing line. Thus, while it was true that almost every finished module met the specification, it was also true that many units had been recycled at various points before they reached the end of the line. "All rework must be taken into account in any assessment of first-pass yield," said Gomersall. "Under the circumstances, your actual first-pass yield is a lot lower than 95 percent. Meanwhile, it's lengthening your cycle time."

Gomersall got out his calculator. "I know from my assessment," he continued, "that there are thirty steps on the module manufacturing line, and there are inspection stations at every fifth step. In other words, steps five, ten, fifteen, and so on are inspection steps. According to Back On Track data, modules are rejected at the rate of 10, 5, 8, 6, 4, and 2 percent respectively from front to back. All rejects are reworked at various stations with a combined total of 3 percent scrap resulting from stations fifteen, twenty, and twenty-five. All rejects found at the final station — number thirty — are scrapped: 2 percent.

"Therefore, the overall "scrap," per se, is 5 percent, which accounts for your first-pass yield figure of 95 percent. But first-pass yield means first-pass *perfection*; so by definition, everything that isn't done right the first time constitutes loss of first-pass yield." Gomersall started tapping the keys of his calculator. "Therefore, your first-pass yield is more like .95 x .90 x .95 x .92 x .94 x .96 or 67.4 percent."

Obviously pleased with himself, Gomersall chuckled. No one else did. When he had paused long enough for the dramatic number to sink in, he pressed on: "Now, consider another issue: product on hold. In this division, 10 percent of your modules are perpetually on hold for some quality question. You're solving the same problems over and over because you have no formal feedback mechanism by which you might use the lessons of experience to cut the on-hold percentage. This brings down your first-pass yield from 67.4 percent to... 60.7 percent! Okay?"

For a moment, the only sound in the conference room was the humming of the air conditioner; even the clacking keys of the secretary's notebook computer were still. "Won't somebody say something?" asked

Moore. "Does anyone think that a first-pass yield of 60 percent is acceptable quality? No? Then answer this question: Why hasn't this process been challenged?"

Before Moore could turn to Lotz, Lotz turned to Rick Jacobs, his divisional production controller. Jacobs cleared his throat elaborately, then spoke: "I think the problem is that, for personal reasons, everyone is happy with the status quo. For one thing, the process ensures that items reaching the end of the line work. In addition, the process promotes Comfortability. Workers are paid according to their output rate whether their work is perfect or not. When Zwick's inspectors snag defects, the faulty units are reworked and credited again to the workers' output rates. And the fact that almost all the items coming off the line meet the spec is good for managers."

"Barriers," Moore responded, "*Barriers*. Two types. What we've got here is a monumental process problem and a cultural obsession with Comfortability that has allowed it to go unchallenged. You've all just seen how process and cultural barriers play hob with performance and measurements, allowing managers to kid themselves while the company gets less and less competitive. There are lots more barriers out there, and we're going to nail them.

"You can also see why first-pass yield is a vital measure of quality. *True* first-pass yield, that is. Lest there be any confusion, we'll track true first-pass yield as an official performance indicator from now on. We'll also rate performance according to cycle time and inventory level. Howie, you may expect a written copy of our assessment and your entitlement goals in three days. We'll talk again at that time." Mustering a dim version of The Headlight, Moore rose. Everyone else did likewise.

Moore asked Gerry Baker and Colin West to stay behind for a minute as the Module people were departing. "I wanted you Marketing and Service people here today because I intend that every sector of the company will embrace Total Cycle Time. At the moment, Nodulex is in a survival mode, so my first priority is to get my cash flow straightened out. I can do that through freed-up inventory and other savings as we get manufacturing to entitlement. Until the cash situation straightens out, my attention will be focused on Modules.

"But make no mistake, your operations are slated for cycle-time reductions within six months. Meanwhile, Gerry, Marketing can help cut inventory by improving the forecasting process. Both Marketing and Services, however, should get an early start by mapping your processes and determining your performance entitlement. When manufacturing looks healthy, we'll swing Total Cycle Time over into your areas. Keep in touch — and get ready. Thanks for coming today." Baker and West nodded and, without a word, headed for the door.

The Howard Lotz family lived grandly in the old Quaker town of Gladwyne, Pennsylvania, a surprisingly rural, carriage-trade enclave just a few Schuylkill Expressway exits north of Center City Philadelphia. Every working day, Howie Lotz steered his midnight-blue Mercedes down a long driveway past the pseudo-colonial stone farmhouse he called home. Turning left, he took a narrow road that forded sparkling Mill Creek (where even a tiny bridge would have invited interlopers), cruised through a few miles of woods and historic, whitewashed buildings, and suddenly shoehorned himself into the seething traffic snarl of the "Surekill Crawlway," bound for Essington.

Because his grueling commute took longer each year, Lotz found himself having to start earlier and earlier to arrive at his desk on time. He gave up his accustomed early-morning jog in Gladwyne, resorting instead to a few lunchtime laps around the seedy Nodulex parking lot. It just wasn't the same. Then the late-summer dog days arrived and midday jogs were out of the question. Just the few steps from his air-conditioned Mercedes to the plant's front entrance were enough to plaster his shirt to his back and darken his mood. Lotz's mood this week was darker than ever thanks to the recent first-pass yield fiasco. He now felt like an idiot for having sent Moore his gruff assurance that the Module Division operated at entitlement. Classy of her not to mention it; if things were reversed, he would have.

Already in a snarky humor, Lotz knew his troubles were just beginning the morning the assessment crossed his desk. He poured himself an herbal iced tea from his midnight blue thermos, closed the office door, and immediately flipped to the last page of the report to see what the damages would be.

There they were in black and white:

ENTITLEMENT OBJECTIVES FOR MODULE DIVISION

1. A MANUFACTURING CYCLE TIME OF FOUR DAYS FROM ORDER ENTRY TO SHIPPING

2. A TRUE FIRST-PASS YIELD OF 98%

3. A REDUCTION IN COST OF 15%

4. A COMBINED INVENTORY — RAW MATERIALS, WIP, AND FINISHED PRODUCTS — OF $9 MILLION (an overall reduction of 50%).

May Day! Was Moore serious? Lotz rooted back through the report to find the timetable for this expected miracle. Good heavens! Eighteen months! Fighting a powerful compulsion to grab the phone, he made himself sit back and read the assessment, page by page. By lunchtime he was as outraged as ever but calm enough to call Moore's office.

"We need to talk," he said.

COMMENTARY

Chapter Three

Ann Moore's initial crisis of confidence was probably excessive but her alarm over cultural attitudes at Nodulex was on the money. It was immediately obvious to her that the company's cultural mindset could erode her effectiveness as an agent of change. No time for wishful thinking. Given the reality of the circumstances and her own lack of command experience, she was probably wise to call in a seasoned, objective outsider. Skill and objectivity aside, Moore knew in her gut that there was no time to waste. Comfortability and other cultural conceits, which had allowed Nodulex to slip into the doldrums, protectively camouflaged many performance barriers within the business process. Only an unattached outsider with years of experience — more years than Moore, in all probability — could prevail against such attitudes.

Besides making the right strategic decision, Moore couldn't have chosen a better problem solver. I myself met Earl Gomersall more than thirty years ago and was profoundly influenced by his know-how. Earl was and is a cycle time guru and a pioneer in time-based managerial concepts that have worked wonders in a number of major corporations. Having "written the book" on time-based techniques, Gomersall practiced techniques that worked again and again. He still does.

The Assessment: A Necessary Component of Performance Improvement

Moore and Gomersall put first things first by assessing the Module Division, pinpointing where the business was and where it could be. Make that *should* be. At Nodulex and elsewhere, however, assessments serve another purpose by giving baseline managers a jolt of what competitive quality really is. Most managers know that for appearances' sake, their yields should be somewhere in the ninetieth percentile, so they often "achieve" that magic number by manipulating or ignoring important factors. Differentiating true first-pass yield from self-serving calculations is almost always an eye-opener.

An assessment's inventory numbers pack a double wallop. One surprise is the sheer size of inventory, the other is its carrying charges — commonly between 20 and 25 percent of value. Because inventory charges are usually carried at the corporate financial level, those numbers may escape notice by line managers. A thorough assessment can change that.

When an assessment is released, its accuracy is almost immediately challenged by in-place managers. Experience has taught me that true baseline performance is usually much worse than managers realize; in other words, the news is almost always bad for the established power structure. Knowing this, I used to strive for utmost precision in determining the baseline-entitlement figures. Recently, I've learned that punctilious accuracy is unnecessary because the time needed to calculate it is better spent attacking barriers. Usually, a baseline figure within plus or minus 10 percent of the actual will do. What's really important for managers to know is that the gap between baseline and entitlement is dramatic. They also must know where the entitlement barriers lie in each of their areas.

Taking the Full Measure of Quality

At Nodulex, Total Cycle Time's debut took the form of a substitute for classic quality-improvement techniques. In view of the company's fixation on quality, Gomersall and Moore elected to sell Total Cycle Time largely in those terms. Here again, time was of the essence. It would simply have taken too long to convince people that competitive processes and good quality were one and the same. To Gomersall and Moore, however, quality meant total quality, a comprehensive *result* of Total Cycle Time rather than a series of specific efforts at damage control.

Although Gomersall's ideas were sinking in, Zwick was still wedded to the piecemeal techniques he had grown to love in previous years. To him, quality possessed a mystique separate from the mundane processes it was supposed to improve. Moreover, it was properly the administrative domain of specialists. Before Back On Track, he had quietly objected to let-Zwick-fix-it attitudes among managers at Nodulex, but he himself clung to that mindset when his old turf was threatened.

Measuring Quality

There is no escaping the fact that quality emanates from responsive performance and satisfied customers. Accordingly, Moore and Gomersall had no patience with measurements that did not address that fact. In company after company, irrelevant measurements have grown like wildfire since the introduction of computerized data tracking and management information systems. The fallacy that if you can't measure something you can't improve it has also proliferated pointless measurements. One CEO recently bragged to me that with a single keystroke he could produce fifty measurements. To what end? I wondered. And how about the people whose time was spent collecting such data?

Those who treat quality as a discrete concept talk about how difficult it is to measure properly. True — so long as it remains isolated from workaday processes. Ironically, that very unmeasurability has kept countless quality programs alive long past their time. Such would have been the case with Back On Track had not a new CEO seen through its self-deception.

The four indices outlined by Gomersall are the ones that count:

- Cycle time
- First-pass yield
- Cost
- Inventory levels

One thing more about these four indispensable quality measurements: They must be applied hierarchically at each level of an operation. No exceptions.

Cycle Time: Finding the Total

Every process has a measurable cycle time. When, as in the Module Division, there are dozens of subprocesses, it may be convenient to take the average work-in-process inventory for a period and the average throughput for the same period, dividing the former by the latter to arrive at a total figure. In situations involving engineering and administration, actions-in-process inventory may be used as the numerator and the out-put rate of actions completed as the denominator.

Cutting cycle time will make a direct contribution to cutting inventory, including the kind not carried in a balance sheet. Furthermore, lower cycle time will effectively reduce the need for finished goods inventory because product can be replenished faster (or if it can be made to order, not replenished at all). As cycle time comes down, the requirement for finished goods inventory declines to little or none, and requirements for raw material are likewise reduced and more predictable.

First-Pass Yield

First-pass yield is one of the most important indicators of high quality. Most managers know this; but unless they use the proper formula to compute first-pass yield, they are lulling themselves into a false sense of security. Such was the case with Howard Lotz until Gomersall invoked the correct formula. Here it is:

$$\text{First-pass yield} = \text{Measured Yield} \times \left(\frac{100 - \text{Rework percentage per step}}{100} \right)^n$$

$$\times \left(\frac{100 - \text{On-hold percentage per step}}{100} \right)^m$$

In the above formula, n = the number of rework points and m = the number of quality hold points. Using Lotz's 95 percent yield figure, and following the above formula, Gomersall's calculations were as follows:

Inspection Station	Rework Percentage (yield)	Yield Percentage
Measured Yield		
Start		95
5	0.10 (.90)	
Yield		85.5
10	0.05 (.95)	
Yield		81.2
15	0.08 (.92)	
Yield		74.7
20	0.06 (.94)	
Yield		70.2
30	0.04 (.96)	
Yield		67.4
35	0.02 (included in reported yield of 95%)	
Cumulative First-pass Yield		67.4
Hold	0.1 (.90)	
Overall First-pass Yield		60.7

I cannot overstress the importance of deriving a true first-pass yield figure. Doing so isn't always easy, as my colleague John Steidl learned in the field. John was involved in an improvement program at a medium-size manufacturing company with operations in the U.S. and the Caribbean. The logistics of moving raw material, work in process, and finished goods between various plants lengthened cycle time unacceptably, but the company was determined to improve quality in that area. A crossfunctional team responsible for improving inter-plant logistics believed that errors in paperwork accompanying shipments were probably lengthening dock-to-stock cycle times. As John recalls, the team "therefore asked each location to measure the other on the number and type of errors in incoming documentation. Oddly, initial results showed an error rate of less than 1 percent. The team refused to accept this number, however, and proceeded to investigate further. What they discovered was that many more errors were occurring but were being caught by the [data processing] operator at the originating location. This operator would then follow up with the originating department to get the error corrected before the shipment went out the door."

Here was a *substitute process* that camouflaged the grim truth about first-pass yield. As John suspected, team members had been measuring final process yield, because "their initial choice of a location for the first-pass yield measurement carried with it an implied assumption about the location of the hidden rework loop. Fortunately, they were smart enough to recognize that something was wrong, and kept digging until they found where the rework was actually occurring. This then dictated the right location for the measurement: in front of the rework loop, not behind it.

"As it turned out, the [data processor] did not really even need to keep an error log [because] she knew the top three assignable causes from experience. The team took this information and immediately went to work on the barriers. At the same time, they asked the operator to begin keeping a formal log in order to verify that their barrier removal activity was having the anticipated impact, and to confirm that no other barriers were lurking in the shadow."

Time and again, while guiding clients in identifying operational barriers, I have encountered another underlying cause of low first-pass yield far upstream in the order entry process.

In a baseline situation, first-pass yield is seldom what it seems.

Reaction to Total Cycle Time

Howie Lotz's negative reaction to the Moore-Gomersall assessment was inevitable and understandable. Appropriately chagrined at his division's low first-pass yield, he nonetheless remained wary of Total Cycle Time because, in his honest opinion, his people were doing their level best and things were therefore in optimal form. The assessment's entitlement figures were simply too big to swallow. If Lotz had his shortcomings as a divisional manager, conscientiousness was not one of them. His reaction is typical of managers when first confronted by the baseline-entitlement gap: they take it personally. But they take it wrong.

Conscientiousness has nothing to do with the problem. Changing mindset has everything to do with it. There are very few companies or components thereof whose baseline performance isn't well below entitlement; in many (especially white-collar) processes, the gap is far wider and the potential for improvement far greater than in the Module Division.

For the new system to succeed, Lotz would have to give it his full support. Winning that support was part of the challenge facing Moore, Gomersall, and Zwick.

Chapter Four

Total Cycle Time
Meets Total Quality

The day Module Division managers met with the assessment team was not designed for creative brainstorming. This summer was muggier than usual, and the outside temperature was so hot that the tarmac of the Nodulex parking lot stuck to the soles of Howie Lotz's shoes. To make matters worse, the air conditioner in the company conference room was emitting an ominous, clattering death rattle. Over in the corner, Ann Moore and Earl Gomersall were having a quiet pow-wow.

"It's not the heat, it's the humidity," said Zwick with a wave as he entered and joined Lotz by the window. Both men were in shirtsleeves. Zwick had the red-rimmed eyes and frogbelly complexion of a midnight oil burner.

"What makes you so chipper?" replied Lotz. "You look lousy! Weren't you supposed to be on vacation in the far north? Oops, sorry! Well, there's always next year. Or is there?"

"That's what this meeting may tell us," said Zwick.

He showed Lotz a postcard he had just received from Bell Island. "Our tenth straight day of cool, bright weather," it read. "Lobster for supper every night. Eat your heart out! Love, Becky." Zwick smiled again and shrugged; then he and Lotz took their seats as other managers filed in.

The presence of Marketing VP Baker and Service VP West indicated that the CEO deemed the meeting strategically important. Lotz felt his resentment rising. Why, he wondered, should the Module assessment be open to outsiders? Baker's high-handed, ever-changing forecasts were more than enough input from that area.

When everyone was seated, Lotz was about to challenge the presence of Baker and West when Moore headed him off, stating that the two VPs had been included at her request strictly as observers. Yeah, thought Lotz, but Gerry has read the gory details. If Mr. Marketing has any gems of wisdom about the assessment he had better keep them to himself. West, too.

Moore started the meeting by polling manufacturing people for their reactions to the assessment, beginning with Lotz. The assessment's brevity had ensured that every Module manager would read it thoroughly. In prior discussion, some had conceded to Lotz that Total Cycle Time looked like more than a gimmick. But that was the trouble. To succeed, Total Cycle Time would require a major refocusing of time and energy, commodities in short supply around Nodulex. Before the meeting, Lotz had made it clear to his subordinates that he hoped to nip this latest interruption in the bud. But he was by no means sure he could do so. Moore seemed ready to go to the wall on this issue.

Knowing from his ROTC days that the best defense was to take the offensive, Lotz immediately challenged the report's generalizations. Reading from his copy, he questioned the statement that process barriers were unnecessarily prolonging cycle time, reducing product quality, and compromising competitiveness.

"Those are pretty strong words," he said. "We're not a bunch of bozos — I'd match our expertise with any competitor — and we don't believe the statement. Can you give us specific examples to back it up?"

Gomersall responded: "We're not impugning your expertise. We're criticizing your business process, which we've taken a hard look at lately. I asked a lot of people a lot of questions; so we can indeed provide the examples you asked for...." The assessment team, Lotz noted, looked prepared to win the day through persuasion, not power. Zwick handed a file to Gomersall, who opened the folder and glanced at the hand-written notes inside as he spoke.

"I'll start with a biggie that goes far beyond your division. The company's computer system is set up to manage on a "push" basis. Forecasts are made, then wheels start turning to ensure that manufacturing starts meet the forecast. Because of that, and because your managers are preoccupied with machine utilization, your lot sizes are too high. I'm prepared to demonstrate to you all that large lot sizes are a barrier to quality and competitiveness.

"Moving right along, you evaluate line workers on the number of parts they produce, not whether such parts are perfect or even required. That's another process barrier. It's generic; I've seen it in a dozen different companies.

"Here's another generic barrier: Overtime is unevenly distributed. The departments in the worst trouble get the lion's share of overtime, which causes resentment among the more effective departments. I'd say you're liable to have a major morale problem on your hands if that doesn't change.

"Here's another. Even though your cycle times are unacceptably long, parts are often in short supply. And when they at last arrive, they often require rework."

If he says "here's another" one more time, thought Lotz, I'll.... At which point, Gomersall laid his itemized notes to one side.

"Before we continue," he said, "I want to mention a different kind of quality barrier in the Module Division. Anybody here know Debbie Poindexter? No? Well, Debbie works the second shift, and she's the best welder in the plant. Welding is a high-tech art here and, as you know, 'leaky' welds are one of the chief causes of defects. Recent records show substantial expenditures have been made to eliminate welding defects.

"I notice that three years back, a trouble-shooting task force determined that defective welding would disappear if every welding machine were refitted with improved power supplies at an overall cost of $120 thousand. The proposal was approved through channels and enacted. Result? A 2 percent improvement in departmental first-pass yield."

"Yeah," recalled Lotz, "it was disappointing and a little embarrassing. But we didn't settle for that. A consultant told us that three-dimensional welding cams would do the trick. It was expensive — $70 K if I recall correctly — but yields did go up further."

"Yes," agreed Gomersall, "but only another percentage point. To this day, one of the sorest spots on the line is welding. Well, after I'd reviewed all this, I decided to talk to someone who knows the subject matter best, which led me to Debbie Poindexter.

"Yesterday, I invited Debbie into this room for coffee and a chat about welding. When things had gotten relaxed, she agreed to let me tape our conversation. I want you to hear part of it." Gomersall switched on a microcassette recorder before him on the table and turned up the volume as the sound of his voice came on the tape:

Gomersall: *"I've heard that your welding equipment was improved. How are things going now?"*

Poindexter: *"Not too good. Briktek's got us jumping through hoops, and that'll mean a lot of faulty welds."*

Gomersall: *"How do you know?"*

Poindexter: *"I take my breaks with a friend who's an inspector. She gives me the scoop about my own units when they come through. It's been hard to fix my leaky welds."*

"Fix them? You know what makes them leak?"

"Sure. It's the little white spots."

"Little white spots?"

"Yeah, on the backs of the units. When we get pressed for a new order, like Briktek's, the units all arrive with those white spots."

"Where do you suppose the white spots come from?"

"They come from the bonders — you know, the hot operation before welding? After the units are bonded, they're supposed to be cooled and then put into white plastic carrying trays. But when the operators are in a rush, which is usually, they skip the cool-off period and plop the hot units right into the trays. The heat melts the plastic, which sticks to the bottoms of each unit. Get it? White spots!" [Sounds of chuckling.]

Gomersall: *"Why are plastic trays being used?"*

Poindexter: *"Back when everyone was on a cost-cutting kick, we switched from stainless steel to plastic trays. The new trays were tested, and they worked okay because the test went through every step of the manufacturing process — including cooling. That was then. This is now: white spots. And white spots make for leaky welds, never mind how good the welding equipment is. Check it out with the other welders."*

"Did you report this discovery to your supervisor?"

"Sure."

"And?"

"And he assured me that the best engineers in the division were on top of the welding situation, so if spots were a problem, they would have fixed it. 'Leave engineering to the engineers.' That's what he told me: 'Leave engineering to the engineers.'"

"So you complied and went back to work?"

"Uh-uh. The spots was affecting my performance, so on the next break, I went to see the bonding supervisor and told her the same story. After all, it was her people that was putting hot units in the trays. You know, I probably shouldn't have put it to her like that. She got what we call a serious attitude! [Chuckles.] She told me the welders were always tryin' to get the bonders in trouble and that she didn't need no advice from somebody who couldn't weld right. That really steamed me."

"So you gave up?"

"No way. By that time, I had a attitude of my own. I decided to go to the inspection supervisor. I mean, it was a quality issue, right? Now, this supervisor is supposed to inspect bonded units before they come to us welders. I asked if he would please reject units with white spots on the bottom and make the bonders scrape them off before they sent them to us."

"What happened?"

"Well, he seemed interested until he looked into his defect book. You know what that is? It is about two inches thick and all it talks about is bonded module units! So he looks in this book and reads out loud all the directions to me: 'Check the shape of the bond, check to see if the bonding wires are centered on the contacts, check to see that the bonded unit is centered in its casing,' stuff like that...."

"But there was nothing in his manual about white spots, right?"

"You got it. He said his hands was tied because the book didn't mention white spots, and it also didn't say nothing about looking on the bottom of a unit! So it was good-bye, quality guy!"

"Pretty discouraging. So you gave up?"

"Oh, no. About that time, they started this Back On Track thing, you know? I got picked for one of the quality cells, but when I mentioned white spots, I was told it was outside the cell's area of responsibility. The cell was busy thinking up proposals for new action, more equipment, stuff like that. What I wanted to do was stop something, not start something."

"So you called it quits?"

"Quits? Ha! I could see it was my problem now. On the way home from work one day, I stopped at a drugstore on McDade Boulevard and bought me a penknife. Next day, I slipped it into the welder and whenever I saw white spots on a unit, I scraped 'em off."

"Did the scraping damage the bottoms of the bonded units?"

"Who knows? I know one thing, though: They did not damage this welder's work, 'cause they was gone!"

Gomersall stopped the tape and looked around the conference table. "Most of that is self-explanatory. You have to give Debbie Poindexter credit for trying to fix a quality problem. But consider this: from the day she figured out the white-spot problem to the day she bought the penknife, seven months had elapsed. As near as I can figure, white spots were costing Nodulex more than a thousand dollars a day — every day. And consider this: since Debbie works only one shift, how many white-spot units are snarling up the process even as we speak?

"Now before we all get tangled in the whys and wherefores of white spots, I have a couple of points to make. Obviously, the bonding-welding process was haywire. When Debbie found herself repeatedly bumping against the proverbial cement ceiling, she innovated a substitute process: the penknife.

"Substitute processes are steps people take to fight barriers rooted in the business process. Substitute processes provide a pathway for innovative people to circumvent root-cause barriers, but they're dangerous because they're an alternative to fixing the root cause.

"Debbie's penknife was a creative solution to a major problem; but once she had found a makeshift way around that barrier, no further attention was paid to its root causes, which have yet to be uprooted. However justifiable its creation, a substitute process is in fact a barrier. The white spot fiasco was at first a subject-matter problem. But it graduated into a business process problem and, left unattended, evolved into a cultural barrier — because it had been around so long!

"Show me a substitute process and I'll show you a business process in trouble. Are there other substitute processes inside the Module Division? Probably. Like all the other types of barriers, they have to go. And when they go, competitive quality will take a great leap forward."

Nobody seemed to want to discuss white spots further. While Lotz's mind searched for someone to blame, Gomersall turned to a different set of notes. "Now let's address the company's quality fixation head-on," he said. "Here's a rule for quality I want you to write down: *Prevention is always preferable to correction.* Pretty elementary, huh?" Except that this rule was ignored. Back On Track went the other way. As Zwick now knows, Back On Track's added inspection effort lengthened cycle times and thereby reduced competitiveness. Worse, Back On Track concentrated on detecting defects, not preventing them.

"Here's where the story gets interesting. When the Module Division adopted quality cells, the engineering cell saw the light about prevention. Encouraged by Back On Track, engineers proposed a design-of-experiments system which would have detected and eliminated the sources of product defects during the design stage. Proper design of experiments would drastically reduce the need for on-line inspection, which would in turn reduce your cycle time and response time to customers. But to date, the engineering recommendation has gone nowhere. I don't want to embarrass you, Zwick, but it took you more than a month to endorse the cell's proposal. Since its endorsement, the request has apparently been in limbo. Anybody know what happened?"

Lotz knew: "I simply haven't had time to deal with the matter because of the pressure we're all under these days. And, by the way, when and if I endorse the design-of-experiment proposal, it will have to go upstairs for final approval."

"There you are: layers of barriers!" said Gomersall, drumming his fingers on his notes. "Even if engineering had gotten all the requisite okays, it would have made no difference to Back On Track's inspection mania. The manufacturing process and the quality process are both faulty.

"What we've been talking about is the tip of an iceberg. The gap between your baseline and your entitlement is the underwater part of that iceberg."

Gomersall then changed the subject: "Just as it takes an outside perspective to spot barriers hiding under cultural camouflage, it sometimes takes an outsider to broach the subject of Cycles of Learning. Cycles of Learning is a systematic method of turning the lessons of experience to advantage. Like other keystones of Total Cycle Time, it is common-sensical and easy to understand in principle. But for some reason, it has been entirely overlooked at Nodulex.

"Here's how it works: Each time a cycle of activity is completed, it is examined to determine which steps add no value and which can be simplified. Every completed cycle of activity — the fulfillment of a Briktek order, say — offers an opportunity for productive learning.

"Cycles of Learning must be used on a formal basis. To get the entitled benefit, there must be a feedback loop in which the data of the last cycle's performance are systematically studied. In the case of the Module Division, statistical process control equipment can be adapted to provide the necessary data for review and improvement. I'll show you how.

"One of the best things about exploiting Cycles of Learning is that it accelerates results. If the Module Division were properly exploiting Cycles of Learning right now, you'd be getting one learning experience every three weeks. And the shorter your cycle times get, the more learning opportunities there are. When you reach entitlement, you'll be getting a discrete Cycle of Learning every three or four days. No one else in the business will be even close to that. I'm willing to bet none of your competitors use Cycles of Learning systematically. High time you started cashing in on those benefits."

Having said his piece, Gomersall pocketed his notes and Ann Moore took control: "Earl's observations should have convinced you that there's room for improvement. Please, let's have no more talk about things being as good as they could be. I want you to think positively about all this. Look at the improvement potential. Look at how much more interesting your work — and Debbie Poindexter's work — will be when you're not wasting your energy on faulty processes. Look at the cash we'll free up by flushing inventory. Look at the drop we'll get on the competition when we're the fastest, best-quality outfit in the industry."

This woman is wired!, thought Lotz, impressed and suddenly, a little intrigued. Thinking tactically, he was getting two other messages. One was that there certainly was room for improvement. He had no comeback whatsoever to white spots or the design-of-experiment question. Ouch! The other was that holding out against Gomersall's surgical critique and Moore's determination was a losing proposition. He knew the value of pragmatism in tight spots (two marriages, not the Wharton School, had taught him that), so he was beginning to see that his people should cut their losses and buy in if they could do so gracefully. Toward that end, he opened the door a little: "All this talk about processes. I assume that Total Cycle Time has a process, or is a process, correct?"

"Correct," said Gomersall. "It is a multi-stage process called the Five I's." With that, he switched on an overhead projector whose noisy fan, added to the din of the sweating air conditioner, created quite a racket in the conference room. First tapes, now view graphs, thought Lotz. I haven't seen such a dog-and-pony show since...

"Here's the process," continued Gomersall. He placed a view graph on the projector and, using his trademark unlit cigar as a pointer, worked his way down the text, which read like this:

THE FIVE I'S PROCESS

- INSPIRATION — in which corporate leadership is convinced of the need for change and then rallies the entire company to the cause

- IDENTIFICATION — in which baseline and entitlement are calculated or estimated for every cycle and sub-cycle of the business

- INFORMATION — in which training is provided wherever needed on a just-in-time or "pull" basis

- IMPLEMENTATION — in which non-value-added barriers and substitute processes are identified, characterized, and removed to simplify processes, and actions in process are reduced, affording the time necessary to take effective steps

- INTERNALIZATION — in which proper measurements, controls, tools, methods, and attitudes are installed to safeguard the new culture and ensure continuous improvement.

Gomersall explained that the Five I's logically commenced with Inspiration, but did not proceed in a formal sequence. "For example," he said, "there's nothing wrong with implementing an attack on obvious barriers as soon as they are spotted, or internalizing new measurements immediately thereafter, even though the processes of Identification and Information have not begun. Ann didn't wait for formal enactment of Total Cycle Time before killing Back On Track. And I trust that today's meeting has provided some tempting examples of barriers that need immediate action.

"Your division will systematically undergo all five of the I's. It takes all five to do the job properly. The components are mutually supportive and overlap in their application."

Gomersall removed his view graph, and Moore stepped into the light of the whoshing overhead projector. "Now, let's talk about that first I," she began. "I'd like to jump-start Total Cycle Time with a momentous event that would grab people's attention up and down the line. But I don't want to raise expectations too high, and I'm afraid the company overspent itself on the Back On Track barbecue, so we'll content ourselves with less flashy inspiration. This meeting, for example. In every company, Inspiration must flow from the top down. That means senior management must be intellectually and emotionally convinced that Total Cycle Time is the driver of competitiveness. We have to set an example, undertake the proper steps, and empower people below us to act in accordance with the new culture. I'm talking about you guys.

"I can see from your faces and body language that some of you are excited about entitlement while others are still wary. By the time you leave this room, I want you all to be inspired enough to give the new culture a try. Notice that I call Total Cycle Time a culture, not a program. To me, a program is a temporary event. Total Cycle Time is not temporary. It's for keeps, and it requires conscious behavior modification. Let's call it *change implementation* because we will permanently change the way this business operates. Is all that clear?"

"It's clear! It's clear!" said Lotz under his breath. Never long on patience, he had had enough inspiration for one day, maybe even one month. But judging from the nodding heads of his subordinates, it was also clear that Moore's judicious headlighting was brightening the inspirational atmosphere immensely. He stole a quick look at his watch. Did Moore intend to hold court in this stuffy room until noon? That would mean a heavy takeout lunch from Sandwich City ("50 DELICIOUSLY DIFFERENT HOAGIES") instead of his usual health-food ration.

"By way of inspiration," said Moore, "I want everyone here to play a little game I learned at Briktek. Would you all please arrange yourselves on one side of the table?"

As the bemused managers obliged, Zwick dragged to the conference table an enormous carton of styrofoam cups and lids, the sort served in fast food joints. Onto the table he dropped a few felt markers, crayons, sipping straws, and plastic bags. Obviously, this was not lunch.

Then came Moore's instructions: "The game we're going to play is fun. It should teach us all something about cycle time, inventory, lot sizes, and quick response. We're going to simulate a production line using these materials. Your 'line' will be processing and packaging cups in lots of six."

Following instructions, Gerry Baker, seated at Moore's end of the table, began the simulation by removing a half-dozen cups from the carton and handing them to Rick Jacobs, whose job it was to ink two black dots near the rim of each cup. That lot of six then moved to Colin West, who crayoned three vertical squiggles on the outside of each cup and passed the batch to Howie Lotz. Lotz clapped a plastic lid on each and passed them to the fifth player, whose assignment was to insert a straw through the slit in each lid and, when finished, move the lot to the last person on the line, who inspected for uniformity (defective cups were set aside) and then sealed six in a plastic bag. Bagging marked the end of the "manufacturing process," except of course that another lot was on its way down the line, then another, and another....

At first a bit irked by this apparently trivial, undignified exercise, the participants quickly got into the goofy spirit of the game. It took them a while to get the hang and the rhythm of their tasks, pushed as they were by oncoming lots. For example, Jacobs repeatedly inked the dots in the wrong places, causing stops and rework as cups piled up to his left. Moore walked the line, offering words of encouragement. Gomersall stood back, timing the exercise. Zwick, the scorekeeper, stood attentively by a chalkboard, tossing and catching a piece of chalk as though he were flipping a coin.

Once everyone was accustomed to the routine, the line was stopped and its work-in-process (WIP) and reject rate were measured. To ascertain cycle time, a specially marked cup had been tracked through the last lot. Zwick chalked the results on his board:

Lot size	6 cups
WIP	48
Rework	12
Cycle time	8. 24 minutes
Output	24 (3 per minute).

The team was put back to its task, this time working with a lot size of three cups. With less push per lot, performance was noticeably different:

Lot size	3 cups
WIP	48
Rework	8
Cycle time	7.08 minutes
Output	57 (8 per minute).

For the third and final run, Moore changed the lot size from push — multiple units in prescribed lots — to pull — with a lot size of one. Almost immediately, things changed. First, the group was able to complete all its tasks in less space — fourteen feet of table instead of twenty — because no piles emerged to clutter and confuse the table top. And when the operation was measured, the chalked results were startling:

Lot size	1 cup
WIP	7
Rework	1
Cycle time	56 seconds
Output	15 (16 per minute).

After a burst of general surprise and merriment, Moore verbalized the message: "The cup game should convince all of you that a huge gap lies between accustomed performance and potential improvement. What you did just now was remove barriers to more effective manufacturing. You converted from a push to a pull system, taking advantage of the smallest practical lot size. Doing so helped you cut your cycle time. Granted, it's a long way from the cup game to your divisional realities. But do any of you doubt that using the same approach on the Module line would net you the same sort of improvement?"

Nobody expressed the slightest doubt, not even Lotz, who called a meeting on Implementation for the following morning. The same group would gather to identify and prioritize barriers for removal. "I'm going to insist," he said, amazed at the sound of his own voice, "that every divisional employee play the cup game. With the right preparation up and down the line, we should be able to give everyone a jolt of Inspiration." There was general agreement. Well, he thought, the boys and I have certainly earned our hoagie heartburn this morning, but I think I'll skip the free lunch and see if I can find Debbie Poindexter.

"Amazing what a little game can accomplish," Moore remarked to Gomersall a half-hour later as the Module people left the conference room. She was having the last few bites of her specially ordered veggie platter.

"Well, that's inspiration," said Gomersall as he doggie-bagged the uneaten half of his hoagie and snatched up a bag of chips for later.

"They're rarin' to go because they see that entitlement is possible. But they're also tickled by how much fun it was to get quick results in the cup game. The real-life game is more complicated. We'll need to follow up right away with some intensive training so these guys don't lose their momentum. You're right though, inspirationally speaking, that was a strong beginning."

A few minutes later, Moore, Gomersall, and Zwick were strolling past the module line when, almost in unison, the three tipped their heads upward to the huge, blue-and-gold BACK ON TRACK! banner still suspended from the lofty ceiling. "Ancient history, huh?" volunteered Zwick, reddening slightly. "I meant to take that banner down quietly last week. I'll get right on it."

Moore didn't miss a beat. "Leave it up!" she replied, flashing The Headlight. "I told you I was a bean counter by training. Nodulex spent a bundle on inspiration for Back On Track, I'm not about to see it go to waste. Let's use it to leverage whatever enthusiasm still exists for the old quality program into the new quality culture we're about to install. Call it a re-cycle." Zwick couldn't suppress his own smile.

Having completed her last bit of inspiration for the day, Moore nodded goodbye to Zwick and, with Gomersall in tow, returned to her office. The two had just settled into chairs for a strategy session when the fax machine on Moore's desk beeped, growled, and disgorged a message. Moore snatched it, read it, and felt her face grow hot. The anonymous message, transmitted from a commercial copy center, had been handwritten in capitals in the style of a ransom note. It read:

AN APPEAL FROM MANUFACTURING

WE'VE PLAYED FOOTSIE WITH CONSULTANTS
WE'VE FIDDLED WITH HI-REL
WE'VE DIDDLED WITH BACK ON TRACK
WE'VE PLAYED THE DE-LAYERING GAME
WE'VE PLAYED THE COST-CUTTING GAME
HELL, WE'VE EVEN PLAYED THE CUP GAME.
NOW IT IS TOTAL CYCLE TIME....
ENOUGH, ALREADY!
WE JUST CAN'T TAKE ANNY MOORE!!!

Moore imagined fax machines spitting out the same message all over Nodulex. Gomersall snorted. "Aw, forget it, Ann. Somebody needs more inspiration, that's all. Don't waste time brooding over stuff like this."

Moore nodded and dropped the subject. She did, however, stash the message in her bottom drawer, and over the next several months, not a day would pass without her wondering who sent it and why. She knew she would never learn the answer to either question, but hoped that someday she would laugh about the matter. That would take a while.

COMMENTARY

Chapter Four

More About Barriers: Substitute Processes

Beware the substitute process! Earl Gomersall turned up a classic example of that type of barrier when he talked to Debbie Poindexter. Substitute processes are a special type of barrier:

- They are sometimes temporarily necessary to keep a business running. Unfortunately, they often become permanently imbedded because the barrier that made them necessary is not removed.

- They are often honestly, conscientiously conceived. When a business process gets tangled and the affected people lack the power to take corrective action, creative minds understandably seek detours around the tangle. Substitute processes are often clever ways of ducking the system or beating it at its own game. The greater the dysfunction of an overall process, the cleverer the detour.

- They are sometimes officially sanctioned. When a company attacks superficial obstructions instead of underlying causes of trouble, it often winds up with a substitute process. At Nodulex, Back On Track was an approved substitute process which attacked the *symptoms* of barriers (defects) instead of the barriers themselves. Many quick-fix quality "solutions" are nothing more than substitute processes.

- They consume resources. Finished goods inventory, for example, is a substitute for fast response to customer needs. Resources assigned to substitute processes can often be redeployed against the root-cause barrier without causing the overall process to deteriorate.

- They lengthen cycle times. Because they characteristically add steps to a system, substitute processes increase the burdens of the system they are supposed to be easing.

- They obscure root-cause barriers. By making baseline practices tolerable, substitute processes either draw attention away from root-cause barriers or obscure them further.

I am especially intrigued by substitute processes within service businesses, for it is in that area that they flourish best. Recently I noted an example that is hurting quality and profitability inside a financial service company. Here's how it works: When a company cardholder challenges an item charged to his or her account, the company's policy is to issue about two month's credit for the disputed sum. The usual practice is to settle such credit disputes before the credit expires, which is why the company has a large sum of money tied up in the disputed charge process.

After a brief assessment, it was clear to me that if challenges could be resolved within one week (which seemed feasible), the company would not need to issue any credit at all. The quality of customer service would rise and costs would decline. In this case, challenge credit is a substitute process that shores up a faulty system, ties up resources, and diverts attention away from possible remedies.

Megacycles: The Two Process Loops

The Module Division's cycles and subcycles of activity occurred within two process loops: make/market and design/development. Those loops exist within virtually all companies.

The make/market loop involves all activities concerned with direct customer transactions, starting with an order and ending when payment is received. The design/development loop encircles all steps necessary to prepare new products or services, from the identification of a market opportunity through the preparation of the needed product or service. In today's time-driven world, the key to success is to shorten both loops, thereby improving responsiveness to existing customers and bringing potential opportunities within reach.

The two loops are interdependent, a fact that got lost at Nodulex during the Hi-Rel debacle. Clearly, the simplest, most prudent pathway to ultimate reliability is to design it into a product, not correct errors during the make/market phase.

Design of Experiments Equals Design for Manufacturability

The Module engineering cell's stillborn proposal for design of experiments revealed an understanding that reliability is designed in, not added on. By definition, "reliability" is a measure of a product's effective longterm performance, not simply a guarantee that everything is in working order on the day of delivery. Early acceptance of the engineering cell's proposal would have prevented the Hi-Rel fiasco.

Design of experiments is a discipline that analyzes the probable causes of a developing product's substandard performance and devises a logical set of tests — as few as possible — to help isolate, identify, and eliminate those causes during the design process. Such tests also provide a logical problem-solving process if a product should evince defects during manufacture. A broader, more explanatory term might be design for manufacturability, for the process necessarily involves general comprehension of such issues as cost, labor subcontracting, number of parts, number of suppliers, and testability. As Earl Gomersall pointed out, prevention is a far more satisfactory way to eliminate defects than detection.

It takes serious strategic thinking to develop a series of experiments by which to engineer more reliable products. The Module Division, for example, could make products out of candle wax if modules were intended for one-time use. To go to the opposite extreme, properly lubricated modules made of nickel-cobalt would probably function for half a century, pointlessly outlasting the machines they were built to serve.

Too often, design experiments are self-fulfilling prophecies that lead to the most expensive materials rather than the desired level of performance. Practically speaking, if a test for module reliability was nickel-cobalt performance but at a cost only one step above wax, a good design criterion would have been found. In every case, the key is to find a reliable part that can be measured against a known standard and be given a figure of merit. For example, if a designed module performed at 70 percent of nickel-cobalt but at an acceptable cost, that might well be the right choice.

Cycles of Learning

Everyone in business learns from experience, but few devise a systematic process for this purpose. That is a pity, for Cycles of Learning are among the most powerful tools for boosting and maintaining competitive quality and performance. The principle is easy to grasp. Upon the completion of a task, performance should be examined for clues about the possible improvement thereof. Doing so makes the measurements of a process meaningful.

The key to proper use of Cycles of Learning is cultural:

- A company must *formalize* the feedback loops that nurture the learning process, and it must *evaluate its people* by their effective use of the process.

- Cycles of Learning must permeate every cycle and subcycle of the make/market and design/development loops.

- A Cycle of Learning in one process may well expose a business process or cultural barrier that lurks in other processes as well.

Cycles of Learning should be used in a cross-process manner to accelerate results.

Cycles of Learning accelerate results because each learning episode provides pointers on to shortening cycle time, which in turn shortens the interval between cycles. But there is another nuance that few appreciate: Cycles of Learning drive the experience curve.

As originally refined by the Boston Consulting Group, experience curve theory states that costs fall by a predictable percentage when a business doubles its cumulative volume. The purported reason for this is that increased experience and volume make a process incrementally more efficient. However, when it comes to learning from experience, real life can be more complicated than theory.

Real life can also be more rewarding. If the lessons of experience are systematically examined and exploited as in Cycles of Learning, creative breakthroughs routinely occur. Cycles of Learning accelerate as cycle times shorten, providing more and more such revelations. Because they are exponential, not incremental, such breakthroughs have a profound impact on the experience curve.

- Effective use of Cycles of Learning drives up first-pass yield, which is the best measure of a process.

- The creative breakthroughs engendered by Cycles of Learning are more important than cumulative volume in steepening the experience curve.

- A company that cuts its cycle times in half may well steepen its learning curve by 10 percent — and it needn't stop there.

- Cycles of Learning overcome the tyranny of size. It is not the biggest companies that win, it is the fastest.

A memorable creative breakthrough recently occurred within my own company, Thomas Group, Inc. From our early days, we had found it difficult and time-consuming to pinpoint baseline performance within our clients' design/development loops. Our original procedure was one that worked in the make/market loop: We would inspire people, then set them to work mapping the baseline process. In design/development, finding baseline proved to be extremely complicated. Because each design team had its own way of doing things, deriving a common baseline from all those processes was very, very laborious. We saw no way around this except learning curve experience, through which we would eventually improve our data gathering techniques. We made progress, but not much.

One day, someone made a creative breakthrough: Why did we need a precise measure of design/development baseline at all? Wasn't entitlement, not baseline, the important thing? Of course! Rather than bog down the improvement effort, we decided simply to divide the design/development actions in process by the output rate, verified against actual completion times. That figure, we were sure, was within 10 percent of actual baseline.

Then came another breakthrough: Instead of laboring long and hard to pinpoint design/development entitlement, why not conceptualize a performance level that would set the industry on its ear, then plan the process necessary to reach that level and forget about baseline analysis altogether? We did, and it worked. The new approach revolutionized our design/development assessment procedures and drastically cut the cost and time necessary to start clients' entitlement efforts.

Another creative breakthrough occurred during a cycle time program at a major electronics supplier. In this case, we were determined to improve the quality of the client's billing process and cut its costs in the bargain. After some Cycles of Learning had helped us remove non-value-added steps, it suddenly occurred to us to consider the fact that some customers paid biweekly, others monthly, and so on. If billings were timed to coincide with customer payment processes, cycle time would be minimal. Sure enough, by arranging to have bills arrive just before each customer's check run, we cut about ten days out of the cycle.

The Lot Size Issue

One of the lessons of Ann Moore's cup game was that small lot sizes are a key to high performance. This fact violates the habits and logic of some managers, so it often must be demonstrated if old paradigms are to be broken. The cup game served such a purpose; but in a pinch, I rely upon a few favorite stories that make the point. The one that follows, told to me by my colleague Bob Ralph, requires no special know-how to appreciate.

The scene is Grandma's farm when Bob was but a kid. One Sunday, word got out that the local preacher was to pay a visit, and the news unleashed a flurry of clean-up activity. Bob and his younger sister were assigned the chore of clearing a flock of chickens from the front yard to a spot behind Grandma's barn. As Bob put it, "We set after those birds with more running, hand-waving, hollering, and foot stomping than you have ever seen. After about twenty minutes or so, we both collapsed on a small patch of grass to catch our breath. As the dust and feathers settled we noted proudly that we had managed to move all but two of those chickens onto one side of the yard. Never mind that it was the side farthest from the barn; to us, that was real progress.

"About that time, my father gave us our first lesson in Cycle Time and actions-in-process reduction, though he did not know to call it that. He told us to get on one chicken and, both of us working together, push, pull, drag, chase or carry that one bird back around by the barn, then run and get another one. He said the trick was to not get distracted by all those other birds, just do one at a time. Well, in no time at all, the chickens were back by the barn and the preacher was in the parlor. Our reward was a cool lemonade — and a lesson that often comes to mind when I'm working with engineering managers...."

Or consider the following story, told to me by Len Gillespie. Like Bob Ralph, Len discovered that the small-lot-size approach works in unusual places. According to Len, "The chief operating officer of one of our client companies is an active member of his local chamber of commerce and also participates in other community activities. He learned that the county commission had caused an uproar recently when it announced plans to construct a new jail bordering a residential area. The residents had the usual response and the project was canceled.

"But the county commission still had a problem because federal authorities were demanding more jail capacity to alleviate overcrowding. Their new solution was to purchase several hundred acres of land ten miles from town to use for the jail, and also to expand the county court facilities while they were at it. This would cost tens of millions of dollars.

"The COO began to investigate this problem with a Total-Cycle-Time mind-set. He discovered that 75 percent of the inmates were simply awaiting trial. The others were 'weekenders,' typically drunken-driving offenders who served their sentences only on weekends. He also learned that the 75 percent awaiting trial were being held because the district criminal court convened only once every three weeks. His solution was to decrease the criminal court lot size and convene court three times per week, thereby reducing the jail population. Coincidentally, the courtrooms only used 25 percent of the available time anyway, so the lot size reduction would eliminate the need for courtroom expansion.

"A true cycle-time proponent, the COO considered the weekender program totally non-value-added. Incarceration costs ran $25,000 per inmate per year. Drunken drivers did not require tight security and were certainly not deserving of free meals during the weekend. His solution was to provide alternative punishment such as community service, cleaning litter from the highways, etc."

The COO's plan was so elegant that it was certain to threaten the egos of county officials. Sure enough, reported Len, our hero was told that state law did not permit those forms of punishment — a cultural barrier. Undaunted, he recommended that the county rent a wing of a local hotel (which had low occupancy during weekends anyhow), require weekenders to stay there under guard, and have those offenders pay for their own room. This process might actually become a money maker for the county.

Here was an opportunity for the community to solve an overcrowding problem by shortening the time-to-trial cycle time and eliminate non-value-added punishment. The community could get better service without adding resources, and tens of millions of dollars could be used for better root-cause solutions — head start programs, education, and the like.

Alas, this creative exercise came to grief. It was simply too good to be accepted by the entrenched establishment. When our hero formally proposed his plan, the underlying agendas of the powers that be were exposed, along with their incompetence, of course. "He also discovered a number of cultural barriers," said Len. "The primary one was that politicians *perceive* reward in having new facilities built. It is a badge of honor. The Total-Cycle-Time approach would give the sheriff an image of being soft on law and order. The sheriff was a crusty old-timer from the rural south. He cinched the deal for the new jail and courthouse when he said, 'Build me a bigger jail. I'll fill 'er up!'"

Never underestimate the power of cultural mindset.

The Five I's Process

It bears repeating that for Total Cycle Time to work on a permanent basis, all five of its components must be undertaken. It also bears repeating that although the system logically commences with Inspiration and ends with Internalization, the Five I's should not be perceived or undertaken as a sequential process.

Total Quality Management efforts usually assume that innovative ideas will originate in low-level cells and percolate up to the top with positive results all around. Not so; and this is one key difference between TQM and the Five I's of Total Cycle Time. Cells do provide insight into the subject-matter problems that concern specialists; but few TQM cells are insightful and empowered enough to attack the overwhelming root-cause barriers to improvement. Total Cycle Time works the opposite way. It identifies and attacks generic, not subject-specific, barriers within the business process and the culture. And it insists that initiative and leadership flow from the top down, creating a fast environment where increased Cycles of Learning quickly raise quality and improve competitiveness.

There are a few common, generic *cultural barriers* in industry that have high impact on performance and are, accordingly, difficult to remove. Generic *business process barriers* are slightly less pernicious and somewhat easier to remove. There are thousands of *subject-matter barriers* of low impact whose removal is relatively easy. Where should your priorities lie?

Inspiration

Top-down flow, as Ann Moore said, starts with the first I: Inspiration. Ballyhoo aside, Inspiration requires complete managerial commitment to the principles of Total Cycle Time. That means a willingness to undergo cultural change, to swap the add-resources mindset for the barrier-removal mindset, and to switch to new, nondelusional measurements. If management does not consistently display such commitment by driving improved quality and other performance measures, it can hardly expect its work force to do so.

Like Howie Lotz, many managers are at first unconvinced that their performance potential is as great as the entitlement figures indicate. As results begin to appear, however, acceptance and enthusiasm get a boost. Then, as people are forced to abandon the security blanket of accepted practices for the new culture, anxiety sets in and morale again plummets. This second dip in the comfort index is only temporary. When cycle times fall further and people acclimate themselves to the new, uncluttered environment in which work is more value-added, more interesting, and more fun, morale recovers and surges to unprecedented heights. But this process takes time and requires patient, unflinching leadership.

Because nothing sustains Inspiration like tangible results, people should not have to wait long to see a few. Every process has an example or two of low-hanging fruit: barriers that can be removed expeditiously. Visible evidence of barrier removal is more inspirational than pep talks and slogans.

On the other hand, nothing disinspires like delay. Too often, quality programs blunt people's enthusiasm by throwing an immediate batch of tedious, just-in-case training at them. If you were fired up about improving quality, how would you take the news that the first step would be a year's worth of instruction? Don't make that mistake.

A final word of caution: Don't overinspire. Too many quality improvement efforts set unrealistically high expectations and pump people up with enthusiasm, then allow months to pass without the promised results. That was the pattern Zwick was coping with when Back On Track was canceled. Once people's enthusiasm wanes, it is difficult to revive it.

Inspiration, remember, is a permanent component of Total Cycle Time, not merely an introduction to it. This point came home to me again while attending a recent meeting between a chief executive of a holding company and his subsidiary CEOs. In this case, the subsidiaries had achieved short cycle time and high quality.

That meeting was truly inspirational. First, each CEO reported the impressive improvements his or her company had achieved, which created a collegial atmosphere of peer-group progress. Then the holding company's chief executive spoke. His subject was "Vision 2000."

"I am going to present the way the world will perceive us in the year 2000," he said, and he went on to deliver a prewritten history of the next eight years, including a rundown on how the corporate leadership would be perceived by employees and customers alike, based on improvements yet to come. I saw eyes shine at the prospect of being part of such an exciting future. Meanwhile, the chief executive was instilling in his people the concept of ongoing improvement, stressing that entitlement was a springboard to even more dramatic achievement. That leader is a man who understands that continuous improvement requires continuous inspiration.

Identification

Identification involves the assessment of the business process within the make/market and design/development loops. At the appropriate level, a limited number of crossfunctional teams define the task of each process. Then, if necessary, they map the sequence of actions in process and align those with their connecting business processes.

Much of Total Cycle Time's ongoing Inspiration derives from the credibility of the Identification phase. Meanwhile, the old, self-deceiving indices that rationalized baseline performance have been discredited. Getting people to abandon their previous quality measurements isn't always easy, however.

Many baseline companies rank themselves according to an industry standard. Some are convinced that because their performance is "the best in the business," there is no room for improvement. That is a self-deluding mindset. Unless a company is running at its entitlement, being best in the business is irrelevant. Some good ideas may come from benchmarking, but the main result is the setting of inappropriate, insufficiently aggressive goals.

As mentioned earlier, it is inadvisable to let an improvement effort stagnate while the exact measure of baseline and entitlement is pinpointed. It is far more important to commence Implementation than to make inspired people wait for precise figures. In the case of entitlement, extrapolations from theoretical cycle time and the use of high-low (best case/worst case) diagnostics will quickly provide an estimate that is within 20 percent of actual entitlement. Percy Barnevik, chief executive of the European giant ABB, puts it this way: "I'd rather be roughly right and fast than exactly right and slow. The cost of delay is greater than the cost of an occasional mistake." That's top-level Total-Cycle-Time thinking in action.

Information

Information is the training component of the Five I's. Because Total Cycle Time requires across-the-board rejection of a company's entrenched mindset and the adoption of another, substantially different set of priorities, some instruction is usually needed at every level. Such training deals not with subject-matter specialties but with generic issues such as crossfunctional team effectiveness, process mapping, barrier identification, and removal and the setup of feedback loops to exploit Cycles of Learning.

In manufacturing and service businesses alike, training should not be prepackaged and doled out on a "just-in-case" basis. Such an approach is as faulty as the "push" mentality on a manufacturing line. Instead, training must be on a "pull" basis: tailored to the needs of a situation after the entitlement thrust has begun and provided just in time. The just-in-time (or, as I prefer to explain it, just-after-getting-stuck) approach will equip (not over-equip) people for expeditious barrier removal.

Training should not be confused with results. Recently, my company was asked by a large, technically-based corporation to design a training package in cycle-time reduction. We countered with an incentive-based proposal to implement results in addition to the training. Cycles of Learning in many different businesses had taught us that results, not training, were the key to permanent improvement.

Implementation

Ann Moore understood that barrier removal must commence at the earliest possible moment. Even before her managers had heard of the Five I's, she took action.

Once initial publicity has stirred enthusiasm for the cause, people at all levels are eager to attack barriers. They should be encouraged to do so. Every individual is expert in his or her specialty and undoubtedly knows of a few irksome, non-value-added obstructions whose removal would make life simpler and performance better in that small corner of the world. Why wait?

At the process level, low-hanging fruit can be plucked to achieve substantial cost savings without a lot of change or hard work. Such improvements can come from bloated raw-material inventories, where the simple act of selectively shutting off purchases for awhile can work wonders. Inasmuch as work in process will be reduced, the short-term need for any new raw material (except for custom jobs) is very low.

Crossfunctional teams may expect to find other examples of ripe, low-hanging fruit during the process examination stage. With the completion of crossfunctional mapping, new, more pernicious barriers will be uncovered. When those are stripped away, other barriers will appear.

Such was the case with another of our highly diversified clients. After initial progress had been made, Implementation mysteriously slowed down at most of the corporate subsidiaries. My associates who were involved in the entitlement effort tried every approach: more Inspiration, more one-on-one guidance, outright cajoling. Yet, across the board, the subsidiaries would not commit to entitlement. At that point, we sat down and did a barrier-identification analysis using the fishbone method, which eventually exposed the root cause of the problem.

The underlying barrier, it turned out, was a corporate-wide incentive program for top managers. That program set limits on individuals' yearly incentive compensation, which made managers cautious. In a nutshell, executives knew that if they committed to too high a figure of performance improvement, improvements that fell short of that commitment would adversely affect their annual compensation. When this barrier was removed, the road to entitlement reopened.

The trick in Identification and Implementation is knowing which barriers are root causes of problems and which are simply symptoms that will disappear on their own once an underlying obstruction is removed. Barrier ranking will be discussed in the next chapter.

Internalization

Internalization is the component in which everyone in a company embraces the new discipline, psychology, and values of Total Cycle Time. In some ways, Internalization is the trickiest of the Five I's because it requires vigilance long after entitlement has been reached. Vigilance, in fact, is a never-ending obligation.

Because getting to entitlement takes fifteen months to three years, people logically assume that once Total Cycle Time is in place, it is there to stay. Don't be too sure. Managers and workers do not always behave logically, especially when their former cultural habits were deeply ingrained. Those old, non-value-added steps may have provided Comfortability, to use Nodulex jargon. Or they may have provided a feeling of security against emergencies, as is usually the case with large inventories. Or there may be new people on board who have not experienced the Five I's and have their own ideas about how to run an operation. In these and many other cases, hard-won, lean, Total Cycle Time culture may start to put on weight.

Several years ago, my company oversaw a time-based effort that achieved its entitlement objectives: improved first-pass yield and productivity, lower cycle time, and reduced cost. We happily departed. In less than six months, however, many of the client's entitlement indices had deteriorated 20 to 25 percent! We investigated and realized that we had driven that entitlement effort too strongly. Our team had, in fact, overmanaged, failing to imbue internal management with a strong commitment to use the tools, methods, measurements, and controls so dear to our hearts and so necessary for continuous improvement. In short, managers had grown used to having dedicated outsiders make the commitment, and we had allowed that to happen. We returned to the company, again achieved entitlement, and, through a process of side-by-side guidance, transferred the new culture to the client.

To avoid the backsliding threat, management must install and enforce a new, quality-based, continuous-improvement system of measurements at all levels, in which employees are rated by their improvements in short cycle times, first-pass yield, and customer satisfaction. In addition, managers at all levels must set the cultural example and live by it. No exceptions. At all levels, care must be taken to preclude model manipulation. Measurements of cycle time and its calculation must be clear and enforced. First-pass yield measurements (including where to measure, what should be reported, and what should not) must be likewise.

The Totality of Total Cycle Time

I cannot overstress the point that all five of the Five I's are interdependent. Any quality and performance improvement effort that ignores one or more does so at great peril. Total Cycle Time is a *total business methodology*. It will achieve its promise only if enacted comprehensively.

Getting back to Nodulex, Ann Moore had reason to gloat over the inspirational success of the cup game. It was, as she said, not a bad beginning. But, given their prior experiences in time-driven management, both she and Earl Gomersall knew that the managerial glow of that morning would be sorely tested over the next eighteen months.

Chapter Five

Shooting for Entitlement in the Make/Market Loop

As a steamy, sticky summer gave way to a steamy, sticky fall, the Module Division did its best to redirect employee thinking toward Total Cycle Time. Top managers were intensively trained to lead and drive the cultural change. Moore was very much in evidence, personally undertaking the initial orientation and instruction chores. Though present throughout, Gomersall preferred to work behind the scenes. Zwick, the CEO's nominal spokesman for time-based quality, had developed an awestruck respect for Gomersall's soft-spoken authority. He spent most of his time shadowing Gomersall, never making a move without running it by his mentor.

Because of the late hours he now kept, Zwick had little time for personal reflection. Somehow, Becky and the kids had buttoned up the farmhouse on Bell Island for the long winter ahead. This fall, home life, such as it was, was as different as work. The twins were now away at Albright College, and Becky, busy with pre-school, was usually in Dreamland by the time Zwick dragged himself home. Strange to say, he minded little or none of these changes. He still rankled over his failed getaway to Nova Scotia. He still felt a pang or two about the late Back On Track program, and he was physically exhausted by the end of each long day. But he had to admit to himself that for the first time, work had gotten a hold on his imagination. Something important was happening at Nodulex and he was in the thick of it. On the inside, actually.

Within the Module Division, Howie Lotz also appeared to have come around. He gave Zwick regular assurances that he supported the program (despite Zwick's insistence that Total Cycle Time was a "quality business culture, not a program"). Likewise, Rick Jacobs, Module's production controller, seemed eager to atone for the pernicious barriers which until lately had hidden under the cover of Comfortability. By general agreement, that very term, so long a symbol of pleasantly collegial working conditions, was banished from the management vocabulary. Another point of consensus was that the terms quality and cycle time should be expressly linked in all future training and publicity.

Meanwhile, the division's quality cells were quietly suspended, although their submitted proposals were reviewed by Moore, Gomersall, and Zwick for clues to better performance. Four of the old cells formed nuclei for newly-constituted, crossfunctional "entitlement teams" that would identify entitlement and attack barriers within each make/market subcycle. One team addressed issues in manufacturing, a second covered order entry, a third handled manufacturing engineering, and a fourth wrestled with production control and materials management. Each included people whose contrasting specialties gave them a stake in the process they were examining and, collectively, an overall view of the make/market loop. All were admonished to focus on short cycle time as the key quality objective, all were officially empowered to "change whatever is necessary to assure smoother performance in every aspect of the business," and all were coached to disregard the managerial hierarchy when coming to conclusions. With Lotz's endorsement, Moore made it clear that identifying barriers and pushing for solutions was "an obligation, no matter whose managerial toes might be stepped on."

Each team's first assignment was to undertake Identification by flowcharting and mapping the actions in process of the make/market cycles. After that came the pinpointing of barriers for removal and the reduction of actions in process. Training — the Information phase of the Five I's — would be forthcoming as needed.

Because such a mandate was easier said than done, most team members needed special instruction in barrier identification, delegation of responsibility, proper reporting, and how to get help when confronted by a problem that lay beyond their effective capability. In every case, team members at first proved better at brainstorming long lists of barriers than properly prioritizing them for action. The trick was to identify root-cause barriers — major obstructions deep within the business process — instead of more obvious symptomatic problems which, though irksome, were mere symptoms of root causes.

Guided by Gomersall, one team counted the number of operator errors observed and/or reported on the manufacturing floor. As expected, the list of errors was high, and many operators grumbled about being graded on poor performance.

They need not have worried. Gomersall assured the team that "operator errors" were not the root cause of the manufacturing floor's problems. He cited the matter of engineering changes, a common but inevitable annoyance on the manufacturing line. "In some cases," he said, "operators were building the wrong part because they had been given the wrong instructions." Were faulty drawings therefore the root cause? No. Further investigation revealed that all change requests had to run a gantlet of sign-off approvals before they were cleared for the floor. In the last-minute rush to make proper floor adjustments, improper and unready specifications went unnoticed.

In such a situation, multiple sign-offs served no value-added purpose. They did, however, use up time while every manufacturing change was on hold. This barrier was uprooted by empowering a specific engineer to make necessary floor changes without second, third, or fourth approvals. With that done, symptomatic "operator errors" fell with a bang.

To train people in the art of barrier ranking, Zwick had them classify their listed barriers three ways: as quality problems, cost problems, and cycle time problems. When they did so, quality and cost problems invariably drew more attention and seemed the most urgent, while problems perceived as cycle-time related were few and far between. At that point, the lists were reviewed in light of the time and effort needed to complete a task properly.

Admittedly, Nodulex's long cycle times had required most people to begin their tasks ever farther in advance of anticipated results. Consequently, forecasts were riven with guesswork and, as time dragged by, further mangled by customers' change orders. With the pace of the market quickening, inventory and guesswork had multiplied. The teams were reminded that if a cycle were shorter, action could begin later, when customer needs were more clear, and still be completed to schedule. Moreover, if barriers to short cycle time were removed, the company would be able to take changing customer needs in stride.

Now, looking at their lists, the teams were asked this question: *Which problems would vanish if cycle time were cut in half, allowing people to begin their task later?* In every case, a few cost and quality problems would indeed disappear. These were labeled symptomatic pains and stricken from the action list.

The remaining list of problems was subjected to another question: *If cycle time were cut by half and action could begin later, could any of these problems be managed more easily or at a lower level of effort?* Some, it invariably turned out, could.

A third question: *Which problems would not budge if cycle time were cut in half?* Those were the most likely underlying causes of poor performance, problems that required immediate, concerted action.

When that exercise was over, team members were asked one last question as a sanity check: *If your paychecks were at stake, which root-cause barriers could you eliminate to get a 10 percent reduction each month in cycle time over the next three months?* The barriers chosen became targets for immediate action.

Barriers that resisted immediate action or lay beyond the teams' empowerment level were neither rationalized as immovable nor hidden from higher-ups. Instead, they were "escalated." Moore had assembled a group of VPs, high-level managers, and corporate staff into a new Business Improvement Team, which she herself chaired. The new BIT's primary function was to deal with escalated barriers. If a cultural barrier proved so entrenched as to defy even BIT action, the BIT was to take the matter to the Nodulex board.

By and large, a barrier's suitability for escalation could be determined by its age. According to an agreed-upon formula, if a barrier could not be effectively attacked by the crossfunctional team within sixty days, it was referred to the divisional VP for immediate action. If, thirty days hence, the barrier was still intact, it went to the BIT.

When he heard of his inclusion in the BIT, Zwick thought of its predecessor and doubted its pertinence. "Isn't creating yet another team an example of adding steps to the barrier removal process?" he asked Moore during one of their frequent klatsches in the CEO's office.

"It's necessary," Moore explained, "because some root-cause barriers are bigger than divisional perspectives. Let's face it: Each division and each department within it constitute little empires of authority, pockets of resistance. If, say, Howie Lotz can't make headway within a reasonable amount of time, it's because his problem is either too big or his own silo vision blinds him to the company-wide implications. That's where the BIT comes in. We're changing culture around here. That usually requires crossfunctional resolution, driven from the very top.

"Show me a barrier that's intact ninety days after identification and I'll show you a barrier that only the BIT can crack. Be sure every crossfunctional team member understands that. And remember, Zwick, Total Cycle Time will soon fan out from Modules to the rest of the company. The BIT can accelerate improvement there if it attacks root causes beforehand."

The Module Division's crossfunctional manufacturing team, which consisted of a manufacturing manager, a maintenance specialist, an engineer, and a planner, had noted several bottlenecks. First, even before the excesses of Back On Track, there was entirely too much non-value-added checking. Each foreman counted parts delivered to the next operation, whereupon the receiving foreman did his or her own count. When parts turned out to be irreparably defective, they were discarded without paperwork or feedback. What, then, was the point of the counting?

A second issue concerned procedure. New tools could be obtained only after a foreman had inspected a worn-out tool and obtained authorization for a replacement. What was the point of that time-honored, time-consuming ritual?

Third, the division's incentive system clock started after equipment setup was completed by the operators. Such operators were achieving high performance ratings by producing units during the setup.

A fourth barrier was inventory figures, which were inaccurate because some supervisors hid parts under scrap or at the loading dock so as to have a headstart when the clock started again.

Finally, manufacturing people were being "started" to death under the old push system. As feared, people were optimizing manufacturing's capability to produce in quantity, undertaking large lot sizes without regard for other parts of the overall process such as order entry and distribution. The operation needed a system that worked back to front like the cup game.

Reviewing the manufacturing list, Zwick and Lotz agreed that overzealous checking and tool-replacement red tape could be quickly remedied at a low or mid-range level inside manufacturing. The inventory, incentive, and lot size issues, however, were process barriers requiring division-level leadership. Fixing them would require a strong dose of retraining.

Assisted by Zwick, and remembering the cup game, Lotz froze the load on manufacturing for thirty days so that planners, habitually committed to large lot sizes, could not react. The team revamped the system to operate on a call for demand (pull) basis. Quickly, cycle time started to fall and product flowed faster through the operation. Actually, nothing moved faster; there were just fewer barriers and piles of inventory that had kept things from moving expeditiously. Workers now had more time to devote to value-added tasks. Overall inventory diminished.

Although in theory such improved performance should have raised morale and enjoyment of work, some managers had instead grown restive, even anxious. The disappearance of reassuring inventory made them jumpy, and they challenged the notion that shortening cycle time was good for quality. "Think about it," one had grumbled, "Michelangelo and Stradivarius didn't take the shortest route to completing their tasks. And the difference between rotgut and fine wine is T-I-M-E."

When Zwick related that conversation one bleak autumn afternoon, Gomersall rolled his eyes heavenward and extended his arms in a gesture of infinite patience. "I've heard that sort of thing a kazillion times in a zillion other companies," he said. "Nodulex has a serious cultural hangup that'll have to be attacked outright through retraining. Come on Zwick, let's take a load off. I'll buy you a Coke." They headed for what was euphemistically called the recreation room: a linoleum and cement-block addition to the building that featured formica tables and chairs and a row of snack and beverage dispensers. Every Nodulexer had learned to steer clear of the machine that offered "PIPING HOT CHICKEN SOUP" and, out of the same spout, "FRESH BREWED COFFEE."

Gomersall almost never took a break — he didn't even like Coke — so it was a safe bet he had something on his mind. The Coke machine ate his inserted coins, after which a can of soda clattered and clunked into the daylight. Gomersall handed it to Zwick and tried again. This time, instead of a can, a cascade of quarters jingled into the coin return groove.

"Jackpot!" said Gomersall, snorting with satisfaction as he scooped up the loot. "This could be my lucky day; but I'll quit while I'm ahead."

Looking for a table, Zwick and Gomersall spotted the telltale bald spot on the back of Howie Lotz's head, so they moseyed in that direction. Lotz made as if to escape, apparently thought better of it, and eased back into his chair. The three sat for a few minutes talking about nothing in particular. Then Gomersall absentmindedly withdrew from his blazer's breast pocket a long, black cigar and, without lighting it, rolled it between his fingers. This tic, Zwick had learned, often signaled the beginning of a lecture. Sure enough, Gomersall leaned back, squinted at the ceiling light fixture and began.

"There isn't much to do nights at the airport motel where I'm staying," he said, "so Tuesday I watched a movie on cable TV that reminded me of my army days. It was one of those flicks about boot camp, where a rookie is assigned to KP duty. The mess sergeant shows the kid how to peel a potato with a paring knife. Once the rookie gets the hang of it, Sarge points to a small tub of potatoes and tells him, 'Take as much time as you need, Private, but do the job properly. The men are counting on you,' or something like that. 'Hey,' says the kid, 'KP ain't so bad after all. I've got all day!' Just then, a two-and-a-half-ton truck backs up and off-loads a mountain of unpeeled potatoes!

"With that, the kid forgets about doing the job right and starts chopping the skins off potatoes in order to get the job done. The peeled potatoes are cubes about half their original size, and the climax comes when everyone in the chow line gets a boiled white cube for supper.

"That scene is closer to real life than you might expect. When I was in the army, four of us on KP duty were told to break eggs and dump them into a huge vat used for humongous scrambled egg breakfasts. 'By the way,' said the sergeant, 'take your time. We don't want any eggshells in the mixture.'

"We started breaking and dumping eggs. It was a little sickening but it was fun. It was also a cinch until — you guessed it — a fork-lift truck rolled up with four gross of eggs!

"What were we gonna do? One of my buddies said, 'Hell, the only way we'll get this done is to quit worrying about broken shells.' 'But we were told to keep the shells out of the slop,' I said. 'That was before the egg truck rolled up,' said my buddy. We all saw his point, so we quit worrying about whether breakfast was any good. We got the job done — after a fashion. At breakfast, hardly anybody noticed the shells. The few who did chalked it up to 'lousy army food' and that was that.

"Now, as much as I like to tell war stories to a captive audience, this tale has a moral. When we were faced with that huge inventory of eggs, quality went right out the window. The same sort of thing happens here on the module line every day: When people are confronted by huge inventories, their work is bound to suffer. To some managers, a pile of inventory may be comforting because it implies that there's plenty of future work to do and everybody's job is safe. But don't kid yourself. Employees will think up all kinds of clever ways to get rid of a repulsive pile of work, no matter how much quality may suffer. If you cut that visible inventory, I guarantee your quality will be better.

"Understanding these psychological realities is a more effective way to achieve top quality than talking about how nice it would be to do a good job. And listen to this: Teaching people to understand the direct relationship between high quality and low inventory is part of your training responsibility." Lotz watched as Zwick made a note and inserted it into his bulging, ever-present folder.

Lotz, who had just enough free time left for a quick jog around the parking lot, gestured toward the clock on the wall and rose from his chair, but Gomersall stopped him with a wave of his unlit cigar and continued the sermon. "Howie, here's another real-world quality consideration you might recognize," he said. "As your cycle times approach entitlement, there will be some unavoidable instances of random downtime where people here and there have nothing to work on. That'll drive managers and supervisors crazy, because they've been trained to enforce the concept of 'a fair day's work for a fair day's pay.'

"Downtime phobia explains why companies like Nodulex hire too many industrial engineers and accountants. And it doesn't make sense. In a company like this one, the cost of direct labor is less than a few points' increase in first-pass yield! Yet despite this, the standard practice is to expend more effort measuring labor productivity than improving yield. My point is that managers and workers alike must be *trained* to reject the labor productivity index. It's a mismeasurement. It's part of the big-inventory/big-lot-size/sloppy-work mentality. Get rid of it.

"Employees are usually smarter about all this than managers. In general, workers won't protest big inventories because, without them, they'd occasionally be assigned 'alternate work' by supervisors bent on optimizing labor productivity. 'Alternate work' often means pushing a mop around the floor until inventory builds again. People who are handed a mop when they run out of work will spread their work so that inventory builds up. Don't let that happen! Meanwhile, if managers catch on, they'll increase inventory to beat workers at their own game. Don't let *that* happen, either.

"You can avoid all these performance and quality glitches if you use downtime for crosstraining instead of mopping. Be sure everyone takes to heart the connection between downtime and crosstraining. The mop mentality has to go. Otherwise, your inventory will go up again regardless of cycle time.

"Speaking of connections, do you see the hookup between poor quality and cultural myopia?" Lotz nodded as Zwick scribbled more lines on his things-to-do pad. Gomersall was now completely wound up on his subject. Escape was impossible, so Lotz slouched back in his chair and began popping raisins one by one from a little red box.

"Here's another quality angle you should be aware of," said Gomersall. "In a Nodulex-type environment, workers should be crosstrained regardless of downtime, because otherwise, the good ones like Debbie Poindexter will get bored.

"Know what happens when skilled workers get bored? They start tinkering with the process in order to bring a little variety to their lives. A driller may turn down the number of RPMs to see what'll happen. Somebody else might use her left hand to insert parts even though she's right handed. It happens all the time when people spend too long at a single repetitive task.

"Tinkering with the process produces two bad effects. The first, obviously, is damage to quality. The second is damage to Cycles of Learning, because inconsistency garbles the feedback. And because Cycles of Learning are crucial to competitive quality, crosstraining and boredom-avoidance are even more important at entitlement than at baseline.

"Most people only pay lip service to the principle that increased responsibility is the best motivational tool. Act on that principle. Push responsibility for quality as far down the line as it can go. Assure your people that they can occasionally run out of work without adverse consequences. Assure them that they can maintain their accustomed pace and concentrate on quality. Enforce those promises. Total Cycle Time will accelerate the results."

It was now time for everyone to go. Zwick and Lotz agreed to meet after work the next day to plan accordingly. Gomersall looked at his watch and rose. "Don't you guys have something to do besides sit here and chew the fat?" he said. "Gotta run. There's another GI movie on cable tonight!"

In the weeks that followed, Zwick and Lotz did follow through. Inventories dropped. Workers began to appreciate their dependence upon the work station previous to their own and their impact upon the next operation on the line. Such awareness, when underscored by formal instruction, brought new understanding of the entire process rather than preoccupation with single elements. Morale rose; even the age-old feud between bonders and welders subsided. With performance climbing, engineers could now experiment with yield improvement on the line itself. By the end of the year they were able to complete engineering experiments within a week. That produced improvements in first-pass yield which, in turn, dropped cycle time and material costs.

Removal of some barriers exposed others. When each production line converted to small lot sizes, the unwieldy setup process of the key cutters, critical pieces of equipment, became unbearable. The problem was that whenever the cutters had to be reset for a different type of module, things ground to an absolute halt. Rick Jacobs oversaw intensive practice drills, which reduced setup time from three to two hours, but that was not enough to keep work in process from piling up.

Here was a rare instance where a modicum of expense could perform a production miracle. Instead of disassembling and reassembling each cutter's intricate components, the division purchased and preset several sets of components that could be handily inserted and removed. Total setup time: three minutes! Cycle time took a dramatic dip.

By Christmas, equipment downtime, once accepted as a matter of course, had become a major barrier. Lotz and Jacobs were especially aggravated by the breakdown of crucial hair splitters. Every time one of those machines went on the fritz, half a shift went by before it was up and running again. Undertaking a fishbone analysis of the problem, the team found that splitter repair was usually a matter of a fifteen-minute adjustment. Where, then, did the time go? "Waiting for signatures!" team leader Ed Beckwith told Lotz with a touch of indignation on the morning he cornered the boss with the completed analysis.

Early on, Beckwith had grasped the potential of the new, officially sanctioned empowerment, and he was enjoying every minute of it. "Divisional policy," he continued, "has decreed that the head of maintenance, the engineering manager, and you yourself as VP all have to sign off on a repair before splitting can resume! In most cases, finding some or all of you guys is difficult if not impossible. Meanwhile, the clock keeps ticking."

Lotz hurried Beckwith out of his office with a promise to read the analysis and take immediate action. He was as good as his word. That very day, the policy was changed so that a signature from the engineering manager was all it took to get a hair splitter splitting again.

But the anticipated gains proved very small. Obviously some other sort of process barrier was prolonging equipment downtime. Although some downed machines were up and running inside of a shift, others were side-lined as long as two shifts. Why? Because all the repair people were clus-tered in the day shift — they liked working those hours. Thus, if a machine malfunctioned at the end of the first (day) shift, it would get no attention until maintenance staffers returned to the plant two shifts later. Until lately, this problem had been camouflaged by overabundant inventories, which could keep a shift or two occupied for a day or more. No longer. The bar-rier was overcome by redeploying some maintenance people to the second shift, placing all on call when they were off duty, and authorizing a respon-sible engineer on any shift to summon immediate help if he judged a repair to be insufficient.

Crossfunctional mapping exposed a whopping substitute process within the make/market loop. Two years earlier, when top management was obsessed with economizing, an enormously expensive precision rotor machine had developed the habit of occasionally slipping out of control and making slightly oversized parts.

To fix the problem, Lotz and associates had chosen a "cost-effective solution." An operator armed with a precision gauge was assigned to the rotor machine with the task of separating acceptable from oversize rotors. Rejects found by that operator were later downsized on a polishing machine. That solution had remained in place since its adoption.

There was no hiding the gleam in Beckwith's eye when he laid the team's latest report on Lotz's cluttered desk; nor was there any mistaking the sigh of weary resignation uttered by the boss as he glanced over the findings. "What's the verdict?" Lotz asked Beckwith, trying to save a little time.

"The verdict is that the faulty rotor machine is a barrier to decent quality because rotor inspection and grinding is a substitute process. The guy with the gauge and the guy on the polisher add no value to the operation. Those steps have to go. You said in your memo of...."

"I *know* what I said in my memo of whatever," interrupted Lotz, with eyes closed and his index fingers boring into his temples. "But since you seem so interested in what I say, tell me how to handle this one. What should I tell the inspector and grinder whose jobs depend on that substitute process? Come on, just once, be a manager. What would you say to them?"

"I'd say to 'em, 'You're about to be retrained,'" replied Beckwith without hesitation. "When this company reaches entitlement, we're going to need everyone we've got because business will be that much better. No offense, but you're the divisional VP, not me. At present, I'm not empowered to make decisions like that one."

There's that dreaded E-word again, Lotz thought ruefully. He knew Beckwith was right, of course, but did the guy have to gloat so much? This was one of those days when he wished to hell he was anything but a divisional VP.

Another of Lotz's concerns was the new Module-8, for which a ready market already existed. Module-8 was a me-too item similar to but more versatile than a product a competitor had already marketed successfully. Module-8 had encountered a few design problems but was expected to fit nicely into an expanding market niche.

On Rick Jacobs's say-so, Lotz had agreed to start building Module-8 in lots of a hundred. Then the lesson of the cup game came back to him. Better check this out, he thought. He buzzed Jacobs and Gomersall.

When the three had assembled, Lotz apologized to Jacobs for waffling on a decision and stated the problem outright. Gomersall was already familiar with Module-8. "You're in charge," Gomersall stipulated, "and I hesitate to get involved in direct decision making because I won't be around Nodulex long enough to reap the consequences...."

Lotz hid his impatience, saying, "Nobody's trying to put you out on a limb. We'd just like your ballpark figure about what constitutes an acceptable lot size for Module-8."

"What about an initial size of ten units?" proposed Gomersall.

At this, Jacobs, who was about to take a sip of coffee, spritzed a fine mist over the top of his cup. "Ten?" he exclaimed. "Our cost would exceed the selling price in a lot that small!"

"Well," replied Gomersall, "there's cost and there's cost. What about quality?"

No reply, so Gomersall continued, poking the air with his unlit cigar to punctuate his points. "In your proposed lot size, you'll have to build a hundred units before you get a single Cycle of Learning. If you encounter quality glitches along the way, you're gonna have lots of scrap or rework; that's the nature of an initial run.

"On the other hand, if you build the hundred units starting with two initial lots of ten each, then four lots of twenty each, you'll get six Cycles of Learning by the end of the first hundred. The rapid feedback will accelerate cost benefits of the learning curve and enable you to fix quality bugs, which will have a terrific impact on long-run costs.

"Another thing. If by any chance you've misread the marketplace's requirements, you can adapt or improve the design before you're over-committed to the wrong version. By the way, what's your arrangement with vendors for Module-8?"

"We committed to them for parts for the first hundred units," said Jacobs. "They're already delivered."

"Pity," said Gomersall. "If you'd chosen the small-lot-size route, you could have worked with vendors on a number of orders. That would've given them better understanding and, probably, better quality."

"Well, we're stuck with what we ordered," said Lotz. "Let's hope there are no quality surprises. Next time...."

"Next time, sure," said Gomersall. "But vendors aside, it still makes sense to cut the lot sizes and get those internal Cycles of Learning. It always makes sense. Remember...."

"I know, I know," said Jacobs resignedly. "The cup game. Okay. We'll start with two lots of ten. By the way, Earl, do you ever smoke those cigars?"

"I gave up smoking years ago. Filthy habit!"

Across the Module Division, shorter cycle times meant more Cycles of Learning, which in turn precipitated even shorter cycle times. The most dramatic case involved a miniature module known as Minidule which had always been a troublesome product. Achieving a precise fit between the Minidule's core and rotor made the difference between a working or non-working unit. Engineers found Minidule yield a major headache. Although assembly required only thirty steps, the rotor-and-core bottle-neck occupied ten people. Each Minidule required matched parts, so engineers were flat out trying to get combinations that worked.

There were several problems. For example, each of the ten operators covertly maintained a stash of three days' equivalent work-in-process inventory. Doing so was easy inasmuch as three day's worth of miniparts would scarcely line the bottom of a paper cup. Squirreling away spares assured a constant yield and a guarantee of work. But it also meant that engineering experiments with proper core-and-rotor combinations took more than a month to be evaluated.

The Minidule line characteristically ran at a true scrap rate of 30 percent, five times higher than the average on other lines. Neither managers nor engineers could get to the bottom of the core-and-rotor bottleneck because no one suspected that so many good miniparts made during the last thirty days were being sidelined. Meanwhile, contented with the customary 30 percent scrap rate, operators would "save" good components when the process was running well and "spend" them when the process wasn't.

But when the ironclad order to reduce cycle time came down from above, Line Supervisor Lamarr Hooks correctly noted that cycle time could not improve unless the line's work in process was accurately quantified. Accordingly, after some counting and accounting, he determined that there was four days' worth of inventory even though he was making his daily schedule at the 30 percent scrap rate. Hooks removed the excess Minidules from the line, intending to feed them back in at a later date, and the result was astounding. Cycle time dropped to one shift — at the same output rate.

To the engineers, this change was a heaven-sent opportunity to run their line experiments on a daily basis. Those short Cycles of Learning quickly established the connection between experiment and result. Within a week, yields jumped substantially and the scrap rate fell to 6 percent. Several weeks later, thanks to the feedback from accelerated Cycles of Learning, scrap was at 1 percent.

By mid-winter, to everyone's amazement (even Gomersall's), the

Minidule line had the most competitive quality and response time in the industry. Keeping it that way necessitated a close watch to ensure that operators henceforward resisted every impulse to "salt the WIP."

All through the previous autumn, Gerry Baker, Vice President of Marketing at Nodulex, had evinced a smiling, all-approving, totally passive attitude about Total Cycle Time. But after Thanksgiving, with manufacturing cycle time shortening and module inventories nosediving, he changed his tune. Changing his tune was uncharacteristic for the amiably consistent Baker, and he was not sure how to express his displeasure. He began by worrying aloud to his marketing cronies that the "Moore's Mafia, especially that crackpot Gomersall," were about to ruin his division altogether.

Despite the sociability of his calling, Gerry Baker kept his private life private and was known inside the company strictly on the basis of his professional accomplishments. That, in the eyes of many, put him out of the running as a possible future CEO, though some wondered if Baker saw things that way. Like many other Nodulex executives, he lived far from his office, insulated from Philadelphia's deepening decrepitude. His home in Chestnut Hill was a genteel, stone, French-style townhouse on a mews lined with large sycamores. Twice a year, he took himself on pleasure cruises: to the north in summer, to the tropics in winter. He was said to have been everywhere; yet despite a pleasantly garrulous nature, he regaled neither colleagues nor customers with tales of his exotic travel. He was never a bore.

Baker was, in fact, a winsome, slightly overweight, fiftyish bachelor given to the same Ivy League wardrobe he wore as a Penn State undergrad. He described himself as "an old-style marketing man" and was proud of his twenty-seven years with the company. In keeping with his traditional sales approach, Baker delighted in person-to-person contact with old customers and, to keep in touch, periodically got out on the road. He was extremely well-liked by his staff and sales force, partly because he had recruited a homogeneous group and worked tirelessly on behalf of his people. With few exceptions, his subordinates followed his lead on every issue, and their propensity to dress like the boss was an industry joke. In or out of the company, one could tell Nodulex salespeople — "Baker's Dozens" — by their sky-blue button-down shirts, regimental striped ties, and his/hers dark suits. In the changing world of modules, Marketing morale stayed high.

Baker's office walls were gridlocked with framed citations, awards both serious and humorous, and signed photographs going back almost a generation, and he never let the Christmas season pass without sending carefully chosen gifts to favored clients. Two years earlier, he had dispensed several gross of silver-plated cufflinks made in the shape of the X-nodule, the company's first product. Those unfortunately bombed within the shirtsleeve cultures of his key customers. Next season, however, he redeemed himself by distributing cases of an obscure Balkan liqueur fortuitously named Nodlexina. Perfect; for by then, Nodulex needed a way to soft-soap its restless clientele. This year, the need was even greater. Those and other reminders made Baker all too aware that the good old days at Nodulex were gone forever. He had reason to be nostalgic about times gone by because, until lately, Marketing had ruled Nodulex.

Marketing had ruled because it dissociated itself from the everyday concerns of design and manufacturing. Instead, marketing people established warm customer relationships and pleaded their clients' cases within Nodulex. It was a given in Marketing that the customer was king, and Baker saw to it that that policy was sub-optimized to the hilt. This strategy had worked for years and was now chiseled in stone. Despite the unmistakable hints of changing times, no one in Marketing, least of all Baker, was going to abandon kid-glove treatment of customers.

To maintain the kid-glove strategy, Baker often had to use a mailed fist with Howie Lotz and associates. Baker had learned that, Comfortability being what it was, the Module Division preferred to produce whatever units it found most convenient and hope that Marketing could unload them. Baker would never forget one painful review a few years back when Lotz had asked him outright, "Why can't you sell what we build?" Some people, apparently, didn't get it.

To Baker, the only effective way to handle manufacturing was to spoon-feed the division meticulous business forecasts and encourage bulk hoarding of many product types to ensure that orders would be filled precisely. Lately, however, he had to admit that inventory was getting the upper hand over forecasting. The growing complexity of the business and the need to have the requisite items on hand when orders arrived required Marketing to forecast ever farther in advance. That now amounted almost to fortune-telling; and as good as he was, Baker's crystal ball was getting cloudier by the month. Marketing simply had to think too far in the future. More and more anticipated orders did not materialize as hoped, and those that did were in an unexpectedly different mix. The answer? More inventory. Meanwhile, hope sprang eternal: Not one unit that went into permanent inventory was ever declared unsaleable.

Marketing and manufacturing both suffered from the fact that while units were all the same in principle, there was no such thing as a standard module. Each customer wanted some slight modification that fitted its end application. For example, there were fourteen different kinds of springs that could be attached to the torque converter module, and these could be ordered in any of three different materials: copper, steel, or music wire. To confuse issues further, some springs had to be plated and some coated to withstand atmospheric variables. And springs were only the beginning.

Baker thoroughly understood all of this but, because he didn't want Lotz to solve Marketing's problems, he was inclined to wash his hands of the Module Division's inventory and concerns. It was Marketing's job to please customers — that was a religion to Baker. He and his people therefore did not hesitate to promise the world. Customers deserved it.

Shortly before Ann Moore's arrival, while the company was grasping at straws, Marketing proposed and won approval for a new Quik-Ship program. Intended to be the ultimate in customer response schemes, Quik-Ship promised selected customers that Nodulex would finish and box orders for same-day shipment. Baker and his people knew there was no question of rapid production to order; the answer from the start was to Quik-Ship out of the company's massive and growing inventory. It sounded good and it pleased a few customers, but the additional warehouse space and requisite people expense canceled out the anticipated profits.

Nonetheless, Baker fought for the retention of Quik-Ship because of its advertising glamour. As he put it during another high-pressure meeting, "Quik-Ship opens doors!" To which the embattled Lotz had responded, "Yeah, it opens the doors of more warehouses." Baker was at a loss for a comeback, and in the uncomfortable silence that followed, he realized that Marketing's grip on manufacturing was weakening. His involvement in the Hi-Rel fiasco did nothing to strengthen that grip.

Enter Ann Moore, self-described bean counter. Even before she took the CEO's position, Moore could see that much of Nodulex's financial hemorrhaging was caused by the tremendous draw-down on after-tax capital for the purchase of all kinds of inventories: raw material, work-in-process, and especially finished goods. This of course was contrary to the new culture she intended to impose upon the company. Work-in-process inventory would eventually come down through the cutting of make/market cycle times. However, unless something was done in a hurry in Purchasing and Marketing, the factory would come to a halt.

Thus, early in December, when the Five I's were up and running in manufacturing, Moore met with Red Riordan, Director of Purchasing, and with Baker. The meetings were scheduled in rapid succession, and Moore did not look forward to them.

Alice Riordan got her nickname in fourth grade, when she was mercilessly teased by fifth graders about of her thatch of unruly, carrot-colored hair. Now, thirty-five years hence, her hair was grey but she was still stuck with her nickname. Hair aside, there had never been anything unruly about Red Riordan. She was entirely competent, inconspicuous, and, after more than a decade in the man's world of Nodulex management, humorless. She apparently accepted the reality that she had gone as far as she could in the company.

Upon entering the CEO's office, Riordan remained standing. Her totally deadpan expression, Moore decided, could only have been achieved through massive concentration. Sensing tension, the CEO skipped the conventional ice-breaking and came straight to the point. "Sit down, Red," she said, characteristically choosing the path of familiarity. "I'm going to make this short because we have very little time to get some big changes accomplished. I want to talk with you about our vendor policy."

"By all means," replied Riordan, sitting erect with her hands tightly clasped in her lap.

"Although I'm new here," said Moore, "my homework tells me that as a rule, Nodulex has been a good company for vendors to service. We never complain about deliveries, and we always have raw material for production when we need it."

Riordan relaxed a little: "That's quite right. We're very proud of the way we treat our suppliers. Big Lotz — excuse me, *Mr.* Lotz, your predecessor — had a philosophy that a happy vendor is a good vendor. As he put it, 'Give them plenty of notice and pay them on time.' I've tried to follow that credo." She smiled self-consciously.

Moore did not return the smile. "I'm afraid the honeymoon with vendors is over," she said softly. "We've got to use every tool at our command to turn ourselves around, and that includes help from vendors. Let's talk about time, which, believe me, is of the essence. Can you tell me the average lead time of our raw materials?"

Riordan looked at the floor and frowned, apparently reaching for numbers in her mind. "On balance," she answered, "we run about eight weeks because a lot of our castings come from mill heats. Response time is usually better if the vendor has the material in stock."

"Red," said Moore. "I want you to review and recommend to our suppliers the shortest lead times you think they can handle. We want to order at the absolute last minute."

"Shortest lead times? We have over twenty thousand active parts, including components, subcontracts, and specials. It would take months to do that kind of analysis."

Moore had seen this coming. "Okay, Red, then cut all the lead times in half across the board."

"Across the board? I'm sorry, but one size doesn't fit all in a situation like this."

"Fix the mistakes later when you have the time."

Riordan stared at Moore, not in defiance but sheer amazement. On her face was the look of a person who suddenly realized that nothing would ever be the same again. She rose and looked down at the CEO, who remained seated behind her desk. "I will of course follow your instructions to the letter," Riordan said. "But I may as well be frank. Nodulex will be out of business if we find ourselves unable to buy in advance of our needs."

Time to use a little muscle, thought Moore, who detested last resorts. "You're not excused yet; please sit down," she said, swallowing hard.

Riordan sat on the edge of her chair and locked eyes with the boss. "By your own definition," continued Moore, "you have eight weeks of stock, although I'll bet much of that we either don't need at all or don't need in quantity. The reason you have all that stuff is that the Module Division operates on a make-to-forecast mentality. But the forecasts are usually wrong! What good is it to purchase so far in advance?"

"Well, Marketing wouldn't like any changes..."

"Marketing doesn't run Nodulex. Vendors don't run Nodulex. The *customers* run Nodulex. Red, the days of make-to-forecast are over. I'm instituting a radical, *permanent* change in the way we do things. We'll be cutting cycle times, going to smaller lot sizes, and flushing inventory.

"Look, I don't want to put you out on a limb. Check with the vendors and verify that they can live with the new lead time or that they can stock the things we'll need. I grant that some will be unable to cope with all this. If a vendor needs exceptional treatment, verify that fact and make the best deal you can.

"I'm serious about all this, Red. If we run out of anything, I'll hold your department directly responsible. I should add that the pressure on vendors won't stop with your 50 percent cut in lead time. If suppliers can take that in stride, which I want you to determine, then we'll cut the lead times further.

"Any questions?" Lately, whenever she asked that, Moore felt like a squadron commander giving a Kamikaze pilot his orders. She accordingly braced herself for the rebuttal.

None came. "No questions," said Riordan, rising. Then, with a slight, formal bow (was Red thinking of Kamikazes too?), she turned and walked coolly out the door, carefully closing it behind her.

Just after the office door clicked, Moore's mind did likewise. Riordan's new marching orders were sure to have massive repercussions in Marketing, so Moore figured Riordan would make tracks in that direction. Accordingly, she allowed Riordan time to get to an interoffice phone and alert Baker to the purchasing crisis. When ten minutes had elapsed, she punched Baker's number. Baker's recorded voice took the call: "I'm away on urgent business for one of our customers at the moment," the voice purred, "but your call is important to me. If you'll leave your number or extension, I'll get back to you in a jiffy."

You better believe my call is important to you, thought Moore. Important enough for you to come out from behind that machine. "Sorry you're so busy," she purred into the receiver after the beep. "I'm not too busy to see you in my office *in a jiffy*. Say fifteen minutes?" She hung up.

Exactly fifteen minutes later, Baker knocked and entered. True to his calling, he possessed a headlight as bright as Moore's, a fact that was wasted on neither party. Baker slouched comfortably in the same suede chair the dour Riordan had awkwardly vacated. Although he had almost certainly been warned by Riordan, he looked innocent of any hint that a sledgehammer was about to fall.

"Gerry," Moore began, "we have a problem. It's basic: We take too long to ship our customers the products they want at a price and quality they're willing to pay for. We'll have to..."

"That's why we have inventory," Baker interrupted with a reassuring smile. (So he *had* been alerted!) "Manufacturing is unresponsive, I admit. But Marketing compensates for that via inventory. You know about Quik-Ship. It's great PR, and without it we'd be dead in the marketplace."

"Gerry, please spare me a marketing spiel. I agree with you that manufacturing is unresponsive, although we're fixing that and fast. But using inventory to feed Quik-Ship is nothing more than a workaround. It costs huge amounts of money, and it's totally unsuitable for a varied, specialized product line like ours. Before we get to arguing about that, walk me through the process you use to deal with customer orders."

Baker's perplexed look suggested that he would just as soon avoid gory details, but he obliged: "Well, first we try to ship from stock if we have exactly the right types of finished modules. If that's not possible, which frankly is most of the time, we issue orders to the manufacturing people to assemble special requests from their inventories of semi-finished units."

"Hold it a second. What happens if all the required parts aren't in semi-finished inventory?"

"I was coming to that. When something's out of inventory, we have manufacturing build whatever we need to do the assembly."

"Doesn't that draw capacity away from other orders in progress?"

"I suppose it does... sure it does. But we have to satisfy customers."

"Even if you're robbing Peter to pay Paul? Peter and Paul are *both* customers."

"We have a priority list for situations like that. If, say, Peter is a vital customer, we expedite Peter's order to get the parts we need."

"And Paul gets the shaft?"

"Like I said, in a pinch, Paul is a lower priority. If Paul couldn't afford to wait a bit longer, he should have ordered sooner. Anyway, we cover most of those eventualities by padding our promised delivery dates."

"That, as the saying goes, is a helluva way to run a railroad," replied Moore. "And it is over with. Gone. Now. From here on out, we're going to tell customers the truth about deliveries and impart some order into the chaos your so-called priority system has inflicted on manufacturing."

Baker made no attempt to defend his priority system. Instead, he replied, "We can't level with customers that way. We'd lose them — and our position in the market."

"Such as it is."

"Okay, such as it is."

"Gerry, can you not see that the mounds of inventory, which are essential to Quik-Ship, are contrary to your objective? Lower inventories will simplify life in manufacturing and allow better, more responsive service."

Gerry obviously had given some thought to the matter. "That makes sense in theory," he answered, "but in view of the present pickle we're in, tell me how we're going to get there from here. It sounds like you want me to sacrifice my customer base so you can test an approach that's unproven at Nodulex. Personally, I doubt if it can be done, but in any case, I don't want to forfeit my customers." Baker's voice sounded a little strangled, and Moore was fascinated by his nose, which was getting redder by the minute.

Click: Muscle time again. "Calm down a second, Gerry," she said. Baker did as she asked, crossing his right leg over his left and apparently studying the wingtip detail of his pivoting right shoe. Moore continued: "They tell me you're about as good as they come at marketing. Likewise, I'm about as good as they come at turning this company around. I'll give it to you straight. Hiding behind mountains of inventory jeopardizes everybody's future at Nodulex. We'll safeguard that future by lowering cycle time, which will allow us to provide better service, faster response. It'll also free up some badly needed cash. Meanwhile, you simply must come clean with your customers, which is not the same thing as sacrificing them.

"Being candid in the short run while we lower cycle time won't run us out of business. By my calculations, you have enough inventory for the next six months. Use it. When customers order up something different from inventory, make the whole lot to order, not just the parts. Then tell the customer the truth. Oh, and while you're at it, cut your safety stocks to zero over the next few weeks.

"Here's how it looks on paper, Gerry." Moore slid a memo across her desk and gave Baker a moment to read it. It said

JUMP-STARTING TOTAL CYCLE TIME IN MARKETING

- Cut order entry lead time from ten days to one day, one shift.
  That alone will give manufacturing a one-week jump.

- Fill interim orders from current inventory or semi-finished-goods inventory. That will help drain the swamp of product on hand.

- Install an approved measurement system to report actual cycle times in all areas. The total of those times will constitute your quote time for all products not in stock or under manufacture.

"Gerry," said Moore when Baker looked up from the directive, "If you... that is, *when* you follow this plan, cycle time and quality will get better by the week, and finished goods inventory will go down likewise. With every drop in cycle time, your quotes will improve. Count on it. Response time will drop from eight weeks to seven, then to five, and on and on. You can quote seven weeks as soon as your order entry snags are eliminated."

"Does Howie Lotz know about this?"

"Howie and I see eye to eye. I expect no resistance from the Module Division and neither should you."

For the second time that afternoon, Moore beheld a face filled with confusion. Baker looked right and left like a cornered creature, then spoke in a throttled tone altogether different from his customary agreeable manner: "I'll do this because I have to. But I will not be responsible for the result."

"You will and you won't. You'll be following my directive, and there's enough responsibility here for everyone to share."

"I intend to document everything we've discussed. You'll get a copy; so will the board."

"So be it. Now, you have work to do."

Without another word, Baker bolted from the office, leaving Moore alone to jot down a few comments. She wrote:

> Baker and Riordan have made careers out of
> responding through inventory and forecasting.
> They both understand Total Cycle Time intellect-
> ually but will resist it on what they deem to be a
> practical basis. If not closely watched, they could
> create major problems in order to vindicate their
> position. Riordan will probably comply because

she doesn't stand on principle. Baker, however, is
a major cultural barrier. Are there others?

In the days that followed, there were others, namely product managers who, acting as surrogates for Baker, disingenuously waylaid the CEO to express befuddlement about various customer accounts. Moore was certain they had been put up to it by Baker. A telephone conversation of that type took place between Jay ("Jato") Torres and Moore two weeks later. Although Torres was eastern regional marketing manager, for some reason, Moore had yet to meet him in person.

Torres: "Ann, I'm buffaloed about Spreadeagle Industries' order, and Gerry suggested I talk with you. We don't have the goods in stock to sell to Spreadeagle. We used to have available stock in inventory and we could compete effectively because of it. We've got to go back to that method. If we don't build for anticipated business, there won't be any business."

Moore: "Nice try, uh, Jato, but don't even *think* about going back. It'll be rough for awhile, and a few customers like Spreadeagle may not like it. If it's any consolation, it took Nodulex a lot longer to get into this mess than it'll take to get out of it."

"In that case, how soon can we expect relief from manufacturing?"

"Manufacturing is coming along just fine. You'll get relief as soon as Marketing maps its process, identifies barriers, and removes them. As soon as orders are entered in a logical manner. As soon as order entry takes under a day instead of fifteen, which by itself would improve your responsiveness to customers by two weeks.

"Look, inasmuch as the grapevine is so strong in Marketing, tell Gerry Baker that I expect you people to get your cycle times down to entitlement. I give you my word that by the time your house is in order, you'll have no headaches from manufacturing.

"While you're at it, pass the word to Gerry to see me so we can firm up a plan to compute entitlement in the Marketing Division. If you don't, I will, by tonight." There was silence on the other end of the line. Torres, a reputed smoothie and a survivor, knew when to fold.

"Thanks for the chat, Ann," he said.

"No charge, Jato. I needed someone to put a bee in my bonnet. Call me anytime you have a real problem."

And you will, thought Moore as she hang up. Like everyone else at Nodulex, you Marketing hotshots are going to be dragged kicking and screaming into a whole new way of life. Why, she wondered, is it always white-collar types who resist Total Cycle Time the most?

She did not wonder long, however. For the sake of her own morale, Moore liked to end each work day with a pleasant task, and today was no exception.

Right on time, the quality manager knocked, entered and waited for the signal to sit. Some last-minute detail must have just occurred to him, for he hastily scribbled a note to himself on the cover of his folder, after which he placed his pencil behind one ear.

"This will only take a second, Zwick," said Moore, handing him a thick envelope. "Here. For your folder."

Still standing, Zwick peered into the envelope and withdrew the contents, which consisted of four first-class, round-trip air tickets to Halifax and a prepaid, three-week car rental reservation.

"An early Christmas present," explained Moore. "You were hoping to spend the holidays in Nova Scotia, right? Good. Make it a long holiday. You've earned it.

"And don't worry; I'll save plenty of work for you while you're gone!"

COMMENTARY

Chapter 5

Controlling the Number of AIPs

The Module Division saved itself prodigious amounts of time and effort by prioritizing and escalating the performance barriers it had identified. Taking that approach kept the number of remedial actions in process under control. It also diverted effort away from symptomatic annoyances that would self-destruct once the root-cause barriers were cleared.

Ordinarily, quality efforts are plagued by too many actions in process. Moved by the inspirational message of quality improvement, people attack barriers on all fronts. When it comes to obstructions, everyone has his or her own pet peeve, which often results in a stampede to dismantle obstructions right and left.

In short order, well-meaning barrier removers thus launch a dizzying multitude of actions in process — far too many to achieve decisive results. Many of these AIPs address symptomatic barriers rather than root causes. Accordingly, they constitute a distracting waste of effort. In a systematic barrier-removal effort, many conspicuous and annoying barriers need not be attacked at all but will fall of their own weight when their underlying causes are eliminated from the business process.

Prioritizing Barriers for Action

Armed with its list of identified obstructions to the business process, a crossfunctional team should employ fishbone analysis. In this case, the fish's "spine" is the effect of the barrier under examination. The bones below the spine consist of causative factors; the uppers are whatever substitute processes are in place for the purpose of circumventing the barrier. Why are those processes in place? What are the underlying causes of the problem?

It is absolutely vital to determine whether a barrier is a cause of ineffective performance or is nothing more than a side effect of a larger, generic process glitch. If fishboning fails to clarify the matter, follow these simple guidelines:

- A barrier that will disappear if cycle time is cut in half is a symptom

- A barrier that will diminish if cycle time is cut in half is a symptom

- A barrier that could be removed if team members' paychecks depended on it is probably a symptom

- A barrier that will be unaffected when cycle time is cut in half is probably a root cause

- A root cause that withstands the paycheck test is probably cultural in nature.

Coming to Grips with Cultural Mindset about Quality

As Zwick, Howie Lotz, and other implementers learned at Nodulex, the power of entrenched clichés about quality should not be underestimated. It is very difficult for people trained in traditional quality clichés to accept the fact that streamlined processes, not painstaking, time-consuming effort, drives quality. Likewise, those high inventory levels that are a trademark of long cycle time seem necessary because they have been linked to good customer service. When inventories start to decline, people concerned about prompt response will balk unless it is made clear to them how short cycle time provides a more effective, less burdensome alternative.

Training programs should not underestimate the power of the old clichés, however. Take the matter of overtime, which is frequently and correctly identified as a performance barrier. Alas, overtime is often a corporate institution. How many managers complain that if there were only more overtime, product would go out the door on time? What they are talking about is a just-in-case substitute process, a hedge against long cycle time. How many employees, meanwhile, have come to depend upon that over-time as a financial birthright? In such situations, when shortening cycle times cut the need for overtime, improvement teams must be prepared for the backlash. The mere explanation, albeit correct, that shorter cycle times mean more work in the long run is counter-intuitive.

Another fact traditionalists find hard to swallow is that running out of work occasionally is preferable to optimizing the use of labor and equipment.

The mindset that idle hands are the devil's playground never seems to go away. It has prompted American industry to optimize labor usage despite the fact that in today's world labor is a small percentage of cost. If that culture persists upstairs, it is easy to see why a closely watched supervisor will hand a paint can and brush to a line worker who has run out of things to do. Such practice almost always leads to sub-optimizing a business (even a low-cycle-time business), which is contrary to the objective of competitive quality. In an entitlement company, running out of work is an opportunity for crosstraining. It is certainly less costly than the alternative of accumulating inventory.

Then too there is the barrier of optimizing equipment, which produces excess inventory. I remember a manufacturing case in which a serious, costly bottleneck was permanently broken by the purchase of a $100,000 machine. This wonderful piece of equipment was overqualified for its application, however: It could process 5,000 parts per hour although the company needed only 2,000. Inordinately proud of his new acquisition, the plant manager took pleasure in seeing it run full tilt all day. That was his order to his supervisor. The supervisor, thank heaven, was both courageous and innovative. For appearance's sake, he maintained an impressive pile of parts in front of the sacred machine; meanwhile, he rigged up a warning signal that would flash a red light whenever the boss left his office. When the light went on, our hero cranked the machine up to full speed so that his superior could smile and nod in satisfaction. When the coast was clear, the line was immediately rebalanced. Now *there* was a supervisor with the proper mindset!

If a company is serious about staying competitive, it must drop the impulse to optimize labor and equipment and instead optimize the Three R's: Responsiveness, acceleration of Results, and effective use of Resources.

Time, Training, and Vigilance Versus Old Mindset

With the passage of time, feedback from Cycles of Learning will do their work. People will experience the validity of the new system and the continuous opportunities to improve. Meanwhile, they must be carefully trained and measured according to the new facts of life.

However understandable it may be, knee-jerk resistance and obstructionism by top management is ruinous to the goal of competitive quality. Total Cycle Time constitutes a new company culture; therefore nothing less than full cultural commitment will do. Any perceived flinching or indifference at the top sends a message that reverberates all the way to the bottom.

At Nodulex, Ann Moore apparently recognized the cultural barrier she faced in Purchasing and Marketing. There, top-level resistance was reinforced by powerful substitute processes: long-range forecasting instead of quick response, massive inventories instead of building to order, and juggling priorities to please vital customers in an emergency. Attacking that entrenched resistance and eliminating those comfortable substitute processes would be risky and difficult, but there was no alternative.

White-Collar Quality: Marketing

Gerry Baker had four regional sales managers reporting to him. Because the biggest customers were in the northeast, it was understood that that region's manager, whose office was next to Baker's, was the marketing VP's right hand. So it was that two days after his meeting with Moore, Baker brainstormed with Jay Torres. In shirtsleeves, nervously fingering his paisley suspenders, Baker was pacing back and forth before the seated Torres.

Torres's slouchy posture and languid manner made him a marked contrast to Baker. In other ways, too, the thirty-nine-year-old sales manager was a paradoxical exception to Marketing's conformist culture. Torres favored suits that looked like Armanis but weren't, lightweight Italian loafers, a flashy Rolex, and outlandishly expensive ties; a look that pushed the fashion envelope beyond the ads in *G.Q.* and stopped just short of a gold earring. Torres, in fact, looked a bit like a fashion model and worked hard to complete that image. Lanky and endowed with sculptural cheekbones, he wore his longish hair combed straight back. His body language consisted of a series of practiced poses, and whenever he moved, one could detect the scent of Aramis cologne.

Everyone in Marketing had buzzed about Torres's style but not a soul — least of all Baker — would throw it up to him because that image was a by-product of consistent on-the-job overachievement. From the start, Torres had cut an unorthodox figure but, as if to rewrite conventional wisdom, had set sales records for several years, cementing and massaging his contacts along the way. Nobody else in Marketing could touch him. His savvy and tireless effort had secured him the regional manager's slot. When it came to matters of customer satisfaction, Baker and Torres were more alike than they looked.

"Before getting the rest of the Marketing staff involved," Baker began, "I wanted to bounce my ideas off you, Jato."

"Bounce away."

"I don't think our new CEO understands marketing. For one thing, she's not a people person. Trust me, underneath that glitzy exterior beats the heart of a systems person — if a systems person can be said to have a heart. Because of that, she's absolutely determined to have her way. So, for the moment, we have to roll with her punches and wet our feet a little in this cycle time program."

"Gerry, are you saying we should humor the CEO?"

"I'm simply saying we won't hang our people out to dry. Marketing people need time to accept the sort of discipline Queen Ann takes for granted. Of course, there's no way to tell her that without looking dumb. But, taking all the realities into consideration, I've put together an action plan that ought to get us by."

"Look, Gerry, I haven't actually met, umm, Queen Ann face to face yet, but just talking to her on the phone convinced me that she knows the difference between eyewash and the real thing."

"Who said anything about eyewash? Marketing's official position is that we endorse low cycle time as the route to quality improvement. It remains to be seen whether Lotz's division can get its cycle times down far enough to please Queen Ann and her buddy Gomersall. They're talking about building to order in less time than it now takes to ship from inventory. Doesn't that sound a bit far-fetched to you? If and when that happens — and if it proves to be more than a passing corporate fad — we'll plan how to quote accordingly.

"Meanwhile, we'll demonstrate that our hearts are in the right place by working on the Order Entry Department. As far as that department goes, Queen Ann has a point. I see no reason why we can't shorten our order entry cycle from a week to a day. And if we can, we ought to. Can't hurt, right, Jato?"

"Could help."

"Yeah. Could help. But let's keep our guard up. If the new regime bombs, at least Marketing won't have sold its soul."

"When do you plan to start the Order Entry effort, Gerry?"

"Not me. You. As a further show of good faith, I've appointed you Cycle Time Manager for Marketing. Order Entry is your baby. Get some help if you have to — *only* if you have to — from Zwick or Gomersall. And if cutting cycle time frees up some Order Entry people, I want them transferred to Forecasting where their know-how can do some good. Queen Ann told me she wants better forecasts, but the time's not ripe to add new people. Maybe later...."

Having grown used to additional assignments during the Age of Consultants, Torres stoically accepted his new duties. A chat with Zwick gave him a blueprint for improving Order Entry's performance: First, map the process as it actually functioned; second, eliminate the non-value-added steps. Zwick was unfazed by Torres's comment that manufacturing techniques might not work in a white-collar operation. "Jato," he replied, "every nonmanufacturing unit thinks it's a special case. This works."

"How do you know, Zwick? You're a manufacturing guy."

"Gomersall told me. Hey Jato, try it, you'll like it."

Jato tried it and he did like it. Following Zwick's instructions, he set up a crossfunctional team including clerks, salespeople, accountants, and production control specialists. Being short on time and out of his depth, he empowered the team to prioritize barriers and prescribe corrective action. As a precaution, however, he went directly to Moore, securing her endorsement and a promise that she would intervene if necessary in the case of recalcitrant functional managers. As soon as it was clear that its empowerment was real, Torres's team went to work with a vengeance.

Mapping the process unearthed a few barriers. The team discovered that customer credit was checked twice for every arriving order: at entry and again before shipping. If, as was promised, response time to customers shortened substantially, this process would be redundant.

Then there was the matter of customer screening. Further analysis of customers disclosed that only a few had ever defaulted on payment. That being the case, why not devise a new procedure in which only potentially troublesome customers were subject to screening? A simple computer table which took that into account was designed. No objections to such streamlining were raised, and the resulting changes lopped three days off

Order Entry's cycle time.

By tradition, new orders had to be approved by engineering people before their formal entry, a step designed to detect any changes in a product between the time of its original quotation and the acceptance of the order. All changes, however, were noted on product prints by a revision number. It seemed logical to empower Order Entry clerks to watch for changed numbers, enter the changes on their confirmation forms, and forward only prints with changed numbers to engineering. Thus, by adding twenty minutes to the normal order entry time, six days were dropped from the approval cycle. Amazing!

Electronic solutions removed other barriers. A change in the computer system eliminated the batching of orders for overnight processing in favor of direct entry, and fax machines were incorporated into the acknowledgment cycle to work directly off the main computer.

After three months of concentrated team activity, Nodulex could process a module order in one day or less: the fastest and most accurate in the industry. Moore's written congratulation indicated that Marketing was back in the CEO's good graces. The Order Entry program had run so smartly that Torres wondered if there were similar opportunities to improve white-collar performance. But where?

Meanwhile, manufacturing cycle time was dropping as promised. Torres touched base with Baker about the matter. Wasn't it time to start quoting shorter delivery cycles to customers?

"It's still too early to know if this cycle-time thing is going to take hold," said Baker when the two at last met. "I'm dead set against making promises to customers we might not be able to keep. We'll continue to quote the old seven weeks. If Moore's program relapses or stalls, Marketing will be all that stands between Nodulex and disaster."

So it went throughout the winter and into early spring, by which time manufacturing's cycle time was down to about two weeks. Then, something very perplexing happened: Northeast sales started to tail off precipitously. The same thing, Torres learned, was happening in other regions. Back he went to Baker.

"This could make us look bad," said Baker, reviewing the mysterious slump. "You-Know-Who wants us to explain it to her right away. She'll probably put us on the defensive, so we'd better be on top of the question.

Get on it and find out what the devil is happening."

Torres suspected he knew what the devil was happening, but he confirmed it with several well-placed phone calls. He was right: Customers had noted the difference between Nodulex's promised delivery times, which were long, and the actual delivery times, which were getting short. A few customers had also noticed that higher product quality accompanied fast delivery: defective material reports and returns had all but ceased. As a consequence, customers were pulling in their lead times for ordering modules. They had not gone shopping elsewhere; they were simply taking advantage of the opportunity to order later.

All of which Baker smoothly explained to Moore, with Torres providing moral support, in the CEO's office: "I see this as a temporary problem. For the long run, it means that our customers have noted our improved quality and responsiveness and are adjusting accordingly. They're not deserting us."

Silence. Baker's relaxed posture was that of a man with no problem, but the reddening glow of his nose hinted otherwise.

Moore fidgeted in her chair and puffed our her cheeks pensively, obviously choosing the words for her response with care. In contrast to her early days at Nodulex, she seemed comfortable with long, reflective silences. Then she looked up at Baker and spoke: "Your explanation makes sense, Gerry, except for one thing. With Order Entry and manufacturing cycle times as low as they are, we must look pretty good to potential new customers. Needless to say, we now have the capacity to service them. How soon will the slump be offset by new orders?"

"Umm, well, we haven't marketed quick response."

"Why not?"

"I wasn't sure the improvement would last, and I didn't want customers old *or* new hurt by promises we couldn't keep." Baker looked at Torres for support, but Torres kept his eyes on Moore and his lips tightly closed.

Moore spoke: "'Promises we couldn't keep?' Gerry, promising unrealistic delivery dates was a time-honored practice in Marketing before we got our processes under control. And for several months, you've had enough process data to demonstrate that Total Cycle Time is here to stay. Correct me if I'm wrong: Marketing has failed to exploit our new quality capability. I thought from the results in Order Entry that Marketing had gotten with the program. *Get with it.* Show me that this fiasco at least has had some instructional value."

"Sorry, Ann. We'll, uh, get with it."

A nod from Moore; then Baker and Torres (who had not spoken a word since the initial greetings) scooped up their papers and quickly filed out.

Every spring, Mr. and Mrs. Howard Lotz gave a Sunday afternoon lawn party at their Gladwyne home. It was their way of paying off a year's social obligations, so dozens of Nodulex managers and spouses, not just the select and the elect, were invited. Because the Lotzes were famous for elegant entertaining, and because Howie's boardmember relatives were always present, few invitees failed to attend. This year, an added attraction was Ann Moore, who with Lotz was basking in the boardroom glow of the manufacturing turnaround.

On the morning of the Sunday in question, the air around Gladwyne was balmy and fragrant. Everything seemed to be in bloom. On the expanse of manicured Lotz lawn, an acoustic combo tuned up while, under a striped canopy, a sumptuous buffet was being set out by several silent servers dressed in white. These activities were closely watched by Howie's wife Sandra and by two blonde Lotz daughters already wiggling uncomfortably in their spotless, sugar-and-spice getups.

As the first guests' cars forded Mill Creek (where their hosts had thoughtfully placed a reassuring WELCOME sign) and turned into the long gravel driveway, Ann Moore was steering hell-bent down the Pennsylvania Turnpike in the general direction of Casa Lotz, her weekend of antiquing in Berks County cut short. Peering over her shoulder was an enormous carousel rooster she had bought at auction in Kutztown the day before. For overnight security's sake, she had singlehandedly wrestled her prize to and from her motel room, a toilsome effort that had gotten her off to a late start.

Forewarned about the dressiness of Lotz parties, Moore had taken with her the requisite trappings but, still clad in jeans and a Ben & Jerry's T-shirt, she had yet to make the necessary transformation. No problem; she had done this sort of thing many times and was quite good at it. In fact, she always kept a magic kit in her van for such occasions.

Stopping at a roadside Howard Johnson's, she entered the ladies room, stepped to the mirror and, in a jiffy, applied the necessary cosmetic touches, standing cheek by jowl with two others who were performing exactly the same operation. (Was everybody going to a party today?) Then, with her face on, she revisited her parked van, unhooked a hanging dress and accessories, and returned with them to the restroom. Disappearing behind the door of a stall, she emerged in no time in hose, heels, and her favorite dress, a simple, high-necked, black number that managed at once to be foxy and classy. Moore had searched long and hard for just such a dress. It had made its debut the week before at a benefit for the Philadelphia Maritime Museum, and, judging from the attention she received from VIPs of both genders, she had shopped well.

Catching Moore's reflection in the mirror, one of the makeup appliers turned around and ceremoniously applauded. On came The Headlight. "Well, back to the old grind," said Moore as she swished out the door and on to Gladwyne.

Half an hour later, she forded the tiny creek and swung into the Lotz driveway. She had not intended to be fashionably late, but she was reassured by the sight of many familiar figures dotting the lawn.

Every social gathering filled her with dread of the round of hellos, the ice-breaking small talk, and the creepy, irrational feeling that she was Exhibit A; but this time, meeting the spouses of colleagues made things interesting. For example, Becky Zwicker, a grownup flower child whose long, straight hair and granny dress were straight from the sixties, struck her as irreverently funny and almost gorgeous. Moore was surprised by this but not sure why. Sandra Lotz, a pretty, matronly, nervous woman, was another surprise. She led Moore on the obligatory tour of her over-size home in which a chintz-obsessed interior decorator had had full sway. It was hard to believe any family actually lived in those pristine, color-coordinated, bookless rooms. Bedecked with more gold jewelry than a Burmese princess, Sandra was fascinated by Ann's sole adornment: a tiny, oval antique portrait of a child worn locket-style on a thin gold chain. The child in the portrait bore a striking resemblance to Moore, a fact which throughout the day invited interested questions from other guests and made conversation easy.

Because the party was mercifully free of gushiness and shop talk, the afternoon passed pleasantly. The amenities were as swank as promised but the vast array of munchies failed to stave off Moore's mounting hunger. Then, just before sundown, the mosquitoes arrived and people began to depart. Craving real food, Moore was timing her escape and wondering whether to gobble another bite-size quiche when a low voice behind her said, "Are you perhaps hungry?"

"Famished!" she replied before she realized who she was speaking to. Even before she turned, the aroma of Aramis announced Jato Torres, wearing a cashmere pullover under his linen sport jacket.

"If you don't have a rule against mixing business with pleasure, we could have a bite together. I know a place nearby, nothing fancy...." A proposal like that from a guy like Torres might put some people on guard. What business? What pleasure?

Something clicked in Moore's brain. "Sounds good," she said. "I'll follow your car."

A few miles from the Lotz house, the tail lights of Torres's BMW led Moore's rooster-laden van across a Schuylkill River bridge to Manayunk, a grim, Dickensian town which had lately undergone a touch of gentrification. On Main Street, near the river, stood the United States Hotel, a venerable eatery facelifted for baby boomers. The place was a bit informal for the dolled-up Moore and Torres, but its upbeat, noisy atmosphere was a welcome change from the rarefied correctness of the Lotz party. Moore felt her energy returning. She and Torres ordered big drinks and bigger sandwiches and, for awhile, exchanged humorous quips about the afternoon. The pleasant, drifty conversation tranquilized Moore's wariness about the business and pleasure remark.

By the time the food arrived, Moore was very glad she had accepted Torres's invitation, and he looked the same. But tomorrow was a work day. She said something to that effect, which triggered a whole new topic. "Ann," said Torres, "before we go, I want to say that I've gotten a real boot out of managing cycle time in Marketing, which really surprises me. If I hadn't been handed the assignment by Gerry, I'd never have believed how all that barrier removal stuff could work in white-collar areas. You know about Order Entry. Well, that episode made me wonder about ways to improve quality in the sales force."

Moore repressed a sigh. Today, for the first time in ages, she had totally forgotten about quality and competitiveness; now here it was again. She took another sip of her drink, noticing the glint of an ID bracelet peeping from under Torres's cashmere cuff. The cuff was monogrammed. This man is very well documented, she thought.

He was also talking business, not pleasure. "Selling, like any other business cycle, is a process," he said, casting her a confidential look as though he were confessing an intimate secret. "It's not well defined, of course, but I wondered why it couldn't be mapped like, say, Order Entry. If we could eliminate the generic non-value-added steps from every salesperson's daily grind, it would be like adding a lot of new people to the sales force for free.

"Well, to make a long story short, I had our team map the process. Right off the bat we spotted a few barriers. For example, it was standard procedure for large bids to undergo regional and corporate approval. Know what that meant? It meant that people upstairs who weren't involved in the bid and didn't fully understand it — guys like me and Gerry — had to holy-water a transaction before it could proceed. Holy-watering added absolutely no value to the process. These final approvals would pile up until there were enough bids for me, or Gerry, or so-and-so to handle in a convenient batch. In some cases, batching added a couple of weeks to the approval cycle time. Ridiculous! Yet the procedure was never questioned until last month."

"You're using the past tense to describe all this. Does that mean it is..."

"Poof! Gonzo! Good riddance. Then, somebody on the team — I wish it had been me — remarked that although bidding was a complicated process, it was also inherently repetitive. Yet no Cycles of Learning were taking place. Why? Because each time an important bid came up, a new bid team was assembled for the purpose, that's why. Think of it. Team after team, every one reinventing the bidding process.

"We established a rule that every new bid team must include at least one person from the previous bid team; that way, the lessons of the recent past would not have to be relearned. Now we're working on a formal mechanism we can use to recycle learning to all functioning teams."

Torres made the one-more-round signal to a passing waitress and continued. "Meanwhile, I kept wondering about how to estimate entitlement in the disorganized area of sales. I talked to Zwick about it — incidentally, there's a guy who's come a long way — and he suggested we use manufacturing's technique of high-low analysis: Examine the actions in process of our most and least effective salespeople, and determine what made them different."

"I thought what made the difference in salespeople was talent, or personality or..."

"That's what everybody thinks, Ann. It's true up to a point but no further. Take me: Do I look like the sort of guy who'd be a star salesman in the module business?"

"To tell the truth, Jato, I'd have pegged you for a star salesman in the movie business."

"I hope that's a compliment. It is? Then thanks. Anyway, I *am* a star, and not because I love people or love modules. When I was selling, I worked on my method and deliberately refined it. I've always known that selling has as much to do with process as with personality, but I never followed through. Until lately.

"Speaking strategically, Nodulex Marketing has always operated by very timid concepts of what was possible. Every year, we'd forecast and then set territorial sales quotas based on last year's performance plus about 5 percent. Using your terms, we'd decide our entitlement using an incremental mindset. But suppose our real entitlement was something far above last year plus 5 percent? How could we calculate true entitlement?"

"You could do it if you understood your process and..."

"Right. Process again. In my region, for example, module sales averaged about $700 thousand per sales rep. Before I came in from the cold, I used to do a million five. Last year, my star salesperson, who I don't mind telling you is Cecil Dean, brought in $2 million. Another rep, whose name I will mercifully withhold, landed only a quarter of a million. Now, as you may have noticed, our sales people possess more similarities than differences. So here are two peas in a pod: bright, presentable people with a good attitude and the same opportunities, product line, and equipment; yet Cecil had 80 percent customer penetration and, uh, Nameless had 30.

"After I talked to Zwick, I decided that those two should be guinea pigs for high-low analysis. I formed a team devoted to the high-low question. Then I had the top and bottom salesperson in each region give us a detailed log of every process step they went through during a business day. When we had their processes documented, we probed."

"Did Gerry Baker approve all this? You only manage one region."

Torres grinned. "Gerry didn't have to approve it. He *empowered* me. I'm Cycle Time Manager for Marketing, remember?"

"Oh, right!" said Moore as The Headlight came on. "So what did you find out?"

"Let's stay with Cecil and Nameless as examples. We found out that Cecil, our star, spent very little time on steps that added no value. Take telephoning. All our people spend hours every week on the phone and, frankly, almost everyone fritters away time on wrong numbers, talking about the weather, dealing with secretaries and answering machines, getting put on hold, getting the royal runaround. A problem right? A *barrier*. Now look at the problem this way: *Every phone call is a potential Cycle of Learning.*"

Moore loved people who talked in italics. She leaned closer as Torres continued: "Turns out that Cecil treated every phone call like a Cycle of Learning, analyzing what did or did not happen and making changes to reduce his phone time in the future. He practiced. He taped his conversations. He made notes about which prospects liked to keep things short, and which liked to be chatted up, and which were impatient with technical jargon, and so on. He learned to quickly assess a new prospect, and he lived by his rules. Result? Contrary to conventional wisdom, Cecil spent less time on the phone than any of his regional colleagues! You can probably guess who spent the most time on the phone, ingratiating himself with customers and counting on his personality to do the work.

"The team adopted Cecil's achievement as every rep's entitlement and adapted his and our other stars' methods as a basis for retraining. Thanks to that, salespeople are cutting cycle time, which translates into more opportunities as their productivity rises. Every region now has its own feedback loop. I plan to install a generic loop to cover all regions.

"As for the low performers, we did a fishbone analysis of each to determine why they couldn't meet entitlement. Any performance differences not caused by justifiable business constraints had to be caused by process barriers. We want to get rid of those process barriers."

"What did salespeople say when confronted by all this?"

"They hated it. They were afraid of it, which was no surprise. They also resented being subjected to fishbones and mapping and stuff that seemed irrelevant to sales. Remember, in this game there are lots of self-perceived artists. A good sales rep can have a very tough skin and a very tender ego at the same time. But resistance lasted only until the results started to show, which they did almost immediately."

Despite the incongruous setting, Moore was impressed by all this and said so. By now her CEO persona had switched on, so she added, "I trust you won't be coming to me asking for additions to the sales staff. Marketing always seems to have its hand out."

"Nope. Reaching entitlement — which is $2 mil per rep per year, remember — is something we'll do with the resources at hand. But wait a minute. Was that a trick question? Down the road, business will probably get so good that we'll need new people! Sometimes I think 'new resources' is a dirty phrase in the front office."

"Right now it is. Jato, did you bring me here to tell me about white-collar entitlement?"

"Ouch! Another loaded question. Yes. No. I mean.... I really am excited about breaking through the incremental mindset, and I wanted to share that with someone who'd understand its importance, and you're it. Before long, Marketing people will see that cycle time and quality apply to them the same as everyone else. Meanwhile, desk work has become more fun than it's been for quite a while."

"Interesting. Zwick said something like that just the other day. Well, this has really been fun, Jato. You're not going to put this tab on the company account, are you?" The Headlight again.

"Not on your life," said Torres with a chuckle. "I never mix business with pleasure. Shall we do this again sometime?"

"I want Baker and his henchmen out of my hair!" For emphasis, Howie Lotz smacked the corner of Moore's desk with a rolled-up computer print-out, rattling an antique redware mug filled with pens. Moore had never seen the VP in such a state. "Understand," Lotz went on, "I'm coming to you as a last resort. I've had it out with Gerry to no avail and he knows I'm here. He just doesn't get it. But I'm damned if I'll let my people get sucked back into Marketing's clutches."

Lotz was putting the final touches on a problem he had dropped in Moore's lap. As he'd explained, it all began when Cy Fischer, Marketing's midwest regional manager, approached a friendly foreman in manufacturing about a special order. Fischer wanted a small batch of Multimods built and put into inventory.

Fischer and the foreman, Fred Downs, had enjoyed years of pleasant association, especially in the selling and making of the Multimod, one of the Module Division's most complex and costly products. Last year, Multimod cycle time was the longest in the division's make/market loop: eight weeks. Fischer's chief customer for Multimods was always in a hurry, asking for delivery within two weeks. Luckily, quantities ordered were invariably small. Fischer had been able to keep his customer happy by forecasting Multimod needs far in advance and stockpiling enough for quick delivery, as was customary until Ann Moore rewrote the rules.

During the cycle-time reduction effort, Marketing sold Multimods from accumulated inventory, which lately had been exhausted. Meanwhile, Multimod cycle time had tumbled to less than three weeks. Lotz and Downs expected that one more Cycle of Learning would bring the time down to about two weeks. They waited for another order. When Fischer approached Downs, it seemed at first that the order had arrived.

Fischer, however, did not have a firm order. As he told Downs, he was jittery about the Multimod account and wanted to have some units in stock just in case his customer needed them immediately. When hearing of the shortened Multimod cycle time, he expressed fears about quality and doubts about Cycles of Learning. Fischer then asked Downs, as a special favor, to build and pack several Multimods "for quick shipment." Downs replied that because manufacturing was now done on a pull basis, he had need a formal order. Fischer admitted that there was no customer order; but in the name of good customer service, he offered to supply Downs with a "Marketing order." An order was an order to Downs, who obliged Fischer. The finished Multimods were put into inventory.

A week later, Fischer made a similar request and offered Downs another "Marketing order." This time, the foreman decided that an order was not necessarily an order and took the matter upstairs.

It soon reached Lotz, who blew up. Lotz's people had worked hard and long to cut cycle times and operate on a pull basis. For the divisional VP, the biggest attraction of entitlement was regaining control of manufacturing and eliminating interference of Gerry Baker and his "witch doctors."

Lotz said as much to Baker, adding that the days of inventory stock-piling were over, period. Baker, however, was intransigent and backed up Fischer's actions ("The customer is king and we must be ready!"). After venturing his opinion that Baker wanted Marketing, not the customer, to be king, Lotz stormed out and took the dispute to Moore.

You're right, Howie, he just doesn't get it, thought Moore when Lotz had finished. What she said aloud, however, was, "Your timing is terrific. This is a sensitive issue that needs to be settled immediately, and as luck would have it, I'll be seeing Gerry in an hour or two. For the moment, suffice it to say that your division will build strictly to order — a real order. No exceptions. Be sure your foremen understand that. I'll get back to you."

When Lotz had departed, Moore crossed from her desk to the conversation group and sat rigidly on the suede sofa, her hands absently stroking the contours of the carved gull on the coffee table. In an almost trancelike state, she did not respond to her occasionally buzzing phone and, more than an hour later, she had scarcely moved. Then, a tap at her office door announced Baker's arrival and snapped her back to the matters at hand. Remaining where she was, she called for him to enter.

"Thank you for seeing me, uh, Ann," said Baker as he took the adjoining chair and spread out some notes on the glass-topped coffee table. Baker's manner was cheerful. "As you know, I'm here to discuss the matter of my forecasters."

"Your what?"

"Forecasters. Didn't you get my memo? I'm here to challenge your directive — is it a directive? — that I cut the forecasting department in half. Ann, I'm frankly amazed that you would take such a position. Just a few months ago you advised me to improve forecasting. Granted, my people haven't always been on the money, but with such long lead times to work with, our record is pretty impressive. In any case, I'm sure that our two new statisticians will vastly improve our accuracy in the future. I'm here to ask that forecasting remain at full force. These are really great people." Baker smiled and waited for Moore's agreeable response. None came. Moore watched his smile fade and his nose begin to light up.

He really, really doesn't get it, she thought for the umpteenth time that day. Finally she spoke: "Gerry, we won't be discussing your statisticians or the size of your forecasting staff. A more important issue has come up. I want to discuss why Multimods were stockpiled without a specific customer order." Suddenly, something Baker had mentioned jangled in her brain. "Just a minute. Did you just say you've added people to your forecasting staff?"

"Statisticians. Expert statisticians. They'll make a big difference in long-range forecasting. Needless to say, your instructions to downsize forecasting arrived after I'd done the hiring."

The idea of Baker adding statisticians to optimize an obsolete function struck Moore as so wacky that she had to fight down laughter. "Gerry, I was going to tell you — no, *warn* you — how seriously I view Marketing's repeated interference with the company's turnaround. Specifically, I was going to read you the riot act. I was going to tell you to get with the new culture. Then I remembered that I'd already told you that and you'd agreed to comply.

"Stockpiling Multimods is an unacceptable case of backsliding. We don't live that way any more. Adding statisticians is another case of backsliding. In short, you haven't gotten with it. You know, Gerry, if I were a psychologist I'd say you're too involved with running your division on a personal, feel-good basis, backing your staff and upholding old practices."

"I believe in my people, Ann. I like them. I motivate them. I believe that good, motivated people can deal effectively with challenge, provided they're not hamstrung by administrative tinkering. In any case, how to manage forecasting properly is my decision, not yours. With the new statisticians on board, I'll match my people against any in the industry. If I determine that we need a bigger department, that ought to be good enough. There's a principle involved here."

"A principle? You're still missing the point, which is that we don't *need* a bigger department, because our response time to customers is never going to be more than a couple of weeks. Gerry, you're beginning to sound positively... *territorial!*"

Baker blinked at Moore's comment, then swallowed hard. For an instant, Moore could hear air whistling in his nostrils. "I'm not sure what you mean," he replied at last. "No disrespect intended, Ms. Moore, but I was prepared to talk about improving the quality of forecasting. I object to being distracted from that matter. Quality forecasting is part of quality customer service. I feel deeply about this, so I'll put it to you this way. Unless I'm given freedom to retain and expand the forecasting function, I'll resign."

Click!

"It is a deal," said Moore.

"Then I'm in control of forecasting?"

"No, you resign. I accept your resignation. A man as protective as you are of subordinates, and with your record of devoted service, should have no trouble finding a more congenial environment. Let's see... it's the eleventh. May we agree that you'll have vacated your office by the thirtieth? You might find it less awkward removing your personal items during evenings when things are fairly quiet around here. I'll alert Personnel to work out the severance details, and we'll of course talk again before the end of the month."

"I don't understand," said Baker, rising. "Isn't this a bit precipitous?" There was that whistling again; it made Moore's skin crawl.

"It is not the least bit precipitous," She said, "And I realize that you don't understand. Call it a cultural conflict — a root-cause barrier — that's been growing for a long time. Gerry, cultural inspiration flows from the top down, and Marketing people take their cues from you. If you're resistant to the new mindset, most of your people will be too. We can't afford that.

"Perhaps when you've had time to reflect, you'll understand. Better still, come back and take a look in a year. The results will speak for themselves. Good luck."

When the door snapped shut behind Baker, Moore felt at once better and worse than she had in weeks. After her hands had stopped shaking, she checked her phone index and punched a number. "Jato," she said when her party answered, "Something unexpected has come up. Could we meet for a sandwich at the United States Hotel tonight at, say, eight? It is a business matter, but I think you'll find it a pleasure, too."

COMMENTARY

Chapter Six

Improving White Collar Quality

Each in his own way, Gerry Baker and Jay Torres learned that most white collar employees consider themselves beyond the reach of systematic improvement methods. Granted that such techniques can turn around a manufacturing situation; what have they got to do with a design department, say, or a sales force, or a service division?

Plenty. Although it is hard to sell, the truth is that every established process has its barriers, which can be detected, ranked, and eliminated. Furthermore, such process barriers, being generic, turn up in all sorts of white-collar operations: sales staffs, accounting departments, consulting firms, software developers, law offices, hospital administrations, or what have you.

The collective assumption that corporate white-collar processes are not amenable to generic solutions is an example of a whopping cultural barrier. And because such processes are seldom examined with anything approaching the scrutiny given to blue-collar operations, the gap between white-collar baseline and entitlement is almost always huge.

Characteristically, white-collar employees and the people who manage them operate under an incremental mindset, measuring this year's performance and tacking on a percentage of improvement as next year's forecast, never dreaming of the performance level they might achieve if they could disentangle themselves from their bad habits. It is just such people who will reap the most improvement from adopting Total Cycle Time.

Sales and Marketing: It Can Happen Here

Inside Nodulex, when Marketing VP Gerry Baker palmed off his cycle time assignment to Jay Torres, he unwittingly did the company a great service, for Torres was perhaps the only marketing manager with enough managerial pragmatism to recognize the improvement potential of Total Cycle

Time. Stimulated by his success in cutting cycle time in the order entry process, Torres quickly applied the technique of high-low analysis to the sales force. In doing so, he was bound to get considerable pushback from his sales people, virtuosos all, who were already annoyed by corporate interference and red tape. However, when the beneficial results of simplified processes, more free time to pursue customers, and systematic techniques for improved salesmanship became apparent, resistance turned into support. That was the making of a culture change.

My own experience includes working with an insurance company that was experiencing pushback from an institutional claimant, with a resulting loss of business. The gist of the complaint was that the insurer did not pay off on claims quickly enough. Very perplexing, inasmuch as the company had lowered its cycle times to entitlement. Perhaps the problem lay somewhere else.

After contacting the disgruntled claimant, the company's crossfunctional team found that slow payment was caused by irregularities and delays within the claimants' internal processes. In other words, it took too long for a claim to leave the claimant's premises. The insurer thereupon helped the "customer" simplify those processes. The results for the claimant were a significant reduction in the payback time, improved cash flow, and greater than ever satisfaction with the service received. All in all, a quality solution.

White-Collar Productivity: Work on the Right Processes!

Returning to Nodulex: Because Baker had removed himself from day-to-day direction of Marketing's cycle-time program, the company avoided a strategic error typical of white-collar improvement programs: failure to eliminate substitute processes. In many such situations, substitute processes are perceived not as barriers but as legitimate parts of the business process. What unfortunately results is a misguided attempt to improve performance of the substitute process, a mistake that can have disastrous consequences.

For years Nodulex marketers had refined and expanded the forecasting capability in order to give manufacturing a head start on anticipated orders. The forecasting function, an honest response to Nodulex's overlong cycle times, had become an important strategic component and a whip used by Marketing to flog manufacturing.

Lacking the outsider's perspective, Marketing's crossfunctional team would probably have tried to cut cycle time by simplifying the forecasting process. Divisional VP Baker would certainly have supported such a move. As an outsider, CEO Moore recognized that the entire forecasting function was a substitute process engendered by the company's inability to build to order. Looked at objectively, with manufacturing cycle time approaching entitlement, the need for elaborate forecasting was over. Accordingly, Moore nailed the forecasting function and, in the resulting flap, a VP who had been unable to adjust to the company's culture change.

Financial arm twisting is an effective way to combat entrenched substitute processes. Throwing resources at a substitute process rarely improves that process by an appreciable degree. Yet cutting resources by as much as 50 or 60 percent will not much reduce its viability. The right approach is to quickly and massively throttle resources to a point where deterioration becomes noticeable; then apply those freed-up resources to removing whatever barriers prompted the process in the first place. Inevitably, both the substitute process and the barriers will be eliminated.

If a company is determined to improve the competitive quality of its white-collar components, the fundamentals of Total Cycle Time must be followed:

- Processes must be mapped

- Non-value-added steps and non-value-added time, when identified, must be eliminated

- Relevant measurements — cycle time, first-pass yield, and process cost — must be imposed and internalized.

The abrupt departure of Gerry Baker, a company institution, dramatized that the sacred cows of the old regime were no longer sacred and that Nodulex's future depended on embracing a new mindset. With an important Cycle of Learning in cultural enforcement behind her, Moore was now ready to take her message to the company's other white-collar division, Service.

Chapter Seven

White-Collar Quality and Competitiveness in the Service Sector

A memorable day in the Service Division began when Ann Moore asked divisional VP Colin West to bring one of his departmental managers, Ed Kizer, with him for a "quick update on quality and inventory" in the CEO's office. "I'm not taking lunch orders," said Moore, "so you can count on getting out of here before noon." Moore did not elaborate on what West or Kizer might expect, but it was a cinch the cycle-time bomb was about to drop on the Service Division.

Since the onset of Total Cycle Time at Nodulex, Moore had kept West posted on changes within the Module Division. West was impressed by those improvements; but inasmuch as Service was by necessity free of quality problems, there seemed no need for an improvement effort in his own division. "That's what I thought, too," said Gerry Baker on the day West dropped by to bid him farewell. "Maybe *you* can't think of a way to apply Total Cycle Time, but Queen Ann will. Good luck!"

The Service Division, which began as a spinoff of Nodulex's manufacturing expertise, was almost totally white-collar. Its bread and butter was designing, installing, and maintaining clean water systems for clients that lacked the time or expertise to manage such systems on their own. Most of the division's customers were semiconductor, aerospace, and pharmaceutical plants. Service ordinarily dealt directly with the purchaser, but it sometimes subcontracted as part of a larger construction effort. Because water systems periodically need purification and expert maintenance, the division serviced what it sold, an arrangement that customers found convenient and cost-effective.

Individualized attention in the form of precise response to customer needs was the key to the division's competitiveness. With the exception of control modules, which were built at home in Essington, all the equipment for Service Division designs was manufactured to order outside the company. Perfect quality was a given, not an objective.

West, who was present at the creation of the Service Division and had managed it for eleven years, had explained the quality issue to Moore shortly after her arrival. That encounter had not gone satisfactorily. Because she had once dated a dapper Britisher by the name of Colin West, Moore somehow pictured another person along those lines. She got instead a hulking, rumpled, preoccupied Pennsylvanian. Like a cavalry trooper who couldn't part with his long-barreled Colt, West still wore a slide rule holstered on his belt. His long, livid arms dangled below short shirtsleeves even in winter. A few wisps of whitening hair covered a huge, ashen forehead that reminded Moore of Moby Dick.

It was West's professorial manner and vocabulary, however, that rubbed the new CEO the wrong way. In conversation, West dispensed words like "dichotomy" and "pejorative" and "paradigmatic," and "per se" while holding his hands in a prayerful position and staring vacantly upward as though his mind were on something more important.

Getting down to cases in that first meeting, West patronizingly dismissed the notion of improving quality inside Service. "Quality is easily measured in our business," he said. "It is a matter of megohms and flow. There is no advantage in claiming to offer 'better water' or more of it. Customer needs dictate that water purity and user safety are virtually absolute, so nobody cuts corners. When we respond to a customer's RFQ — that's a request for a quotation — we assume they seek a reasonable, accurate estimate of installation time, performance to specification, low cost, and sound, long-term maintenance. We deliver all of that."

"And well done," responded the smiling Moore. "But the trick is to deliver all of that profitably in the face of stiffening competition. If quality is absolute in your business, someone must be doing something better or you'd have the whole market." West smiled back and nodded agreeably. "Give us more resources, and maybe we'll get it!"

"No," Moore shot back, still smiling. "That's the *other* trick: to increase market share using only the resources you have. That, in fact, is your assignment. Think about it and we'll talk again." End of discussion.

But what, exactly, was there to think about? Now, ten months later, the upcoming meeting might make things clear.

That meeting included quality manager Hirtle Zwicker, a manufacturing type little known to Service people. As he, Moore, West, and Kizer sat in the conversation group, West admired the artful shape of the carved gull on the glass-topped coffee table. Moore acknowledged the compliment by patting the gull, turning it slightly so that its baleful stare fixed upon her visitors. An accident? The CEO then surprised West and the Kizer by announcing that Zwick would oversee cycle time reduction in the Service Division.

Before West could restate his assurance that Service was immune to quality shortcomings, Moore stipulated that she would let Zwick handle the planning details. "However," she said, "something in Service caught my attention lately — an important *quality* detail — which requires your immediate attention. It concerns inventory.

"As you know, Colin, I'm death on inventory. As you also know, Nodulex began its improvement program in the Module Division because we needed to liberate the cash tied up in inventory there. Now, I notice, Service has a similar inventory stash I want to get at. It's in your department, Ed." Moore turned her glance on Kizer. "There's too much inventory in the Projects Department. It's hurting the company and it has to go."

As West's fair-haired boy, Ed Kizer was not accustomed to criticism of any sort. His department, which converted plans into installed systems for clients, was the best run in Service. Over the last few years, as Service's profitability had slipped, Kizer's standing had soared with his peers and with corporate Finance thanks to his ability to bring in large infusions of client front money when an RFQ was accepted. Finance loved positive cash flow, and Kizer's cash flow was a ray of light piercing the dark cloud that hung over Nodulex.

Astonished at being called to account, Kizer took his time before replying to Moore. At last, he spoke: "Projects' finances are better than any other's." Venturing a wan smile, he added, "If the other departments' numbers were as positive as mine, company leadership wouldn't be driven to such extremes as challenging my management."

"Whoa! Don't get defensive, Ed," replied Moore. "I'm challenging your *inventory*, not your cash flow or overall management. You've got too much inventory. Why?"

"The inventory consists of fixtures and equipment we need for our projects," answered Kizer. "And this is important: It is purchased with clients' front money, so it doesn't cost Nodulex a dime. Furthermore, my department doesn't begin to spend all our front money on inventory. My ready cash is always at least a third more than the cost of my inventory, so I'm ahead of the game. What's the gripe?"

"The gripe," Moore answered, "is that in the culture of Total Cycle Time, cash in hand is no excuse to stockpile, because the annual cost of carrying inventory is often more than 20 percent of its value."

At this point, West broke in: "I think what Ann is iterating, Ed, is the macrocosmic picture. According to the paradigm of Total Cycle Time, it is inappropriate for your department to overspend on inventory while the remainder of the division is deficient in cash."

Is this guy for real? Moore wondered. "I'll *iterate* even further," she iterated, throwing in The Headlight. "I'll even *re*iterate. It doesn't make sense for the Projects Department to carry much inventory, period. Projects' inventory, like everybody else's, should be strictly controlled by cycle time. And incidentally, Colin, it would be inappropriate to feed Projects' surplus cash to the rest of your division because your whole operation should control expenses through short cycle time. We're picking on Ed today because his is the department with visible inventory, and I want to flush it. Now. But make no mistake: It's time to apply the same discipline throughout Service.

"Service designs and builds everything to order, so there's no need for any finished goods inventory aside from whatever is awaiting shipment at the moment of record. So kiss it goodbye. Within a year, Service will be operating so responsively, so precisely, that inventory won't be necessary. It's happening in manufacturing; it'll happen in Service. Meanwhile, I need the cash represented by Ed's inventory. Now, let's discuss the division's overall improvement plan. Zwick, would you..."

"Before we get into generalities," piped up Kizer, "I'd like to clarify the situation in Projects. My people have always operated by the rule that if inventory was not higher than front money, we were ahead of the game. More important, the corporate financial staff has always measured me on cash flow. Are you saying that that's over, Ann?"

"That's over. Thanks for reminding me. The BIT will install more meaningful financial measurements."

"Such as?"

"Such as cycle time, first-pass yield, and total product cost. Those are the right measurements for a project-based business. Flush that inventory.

"Another thing," said Moore, returning her gaze to West. "Indifference to inventory management is ingrained here, part of a complex cultural pattern I'm determined to crack. The new measurements I just mentioned, such as cycle time and cost, are a forcing function. The Projects Department now will have to practice inventory discipline. Just the same, old habits die hard, so I want you both to be on guard against a resurgence. Thank you for coming, Ed."

Kizer took the signal, rose, and departed, whereupon Moore resumed her conversation with West. "In the time that remains," she said, "I want to orient you on my quality and cycle-time goals for Service. But first, I'd like your assurance that you'll play ball. Service isn't the first white-collar operation in Nodulex that has had to make that decision. As I'm sure you know, Marketing had difficulty conforming to the new culture. We can't afford a repetition of that. Do I have your support?" Moore was gambling that West, for all his pomposity, was a better abstract thinker than Gerry Baker and would therefore be less resistant to the new wave. Still, it couldn't have hurt to allude to Baker's ill-fated example.

West chuckled and, for the first time in the meeting, looked directly at Moore. "You have my support. I'll do what I can to instill that support throughout my division. But..." West's huge forehead wrinkled as he prepared to equivocate.

"Thanks Colin. I'm counting on you. Now let's get down to cases. Zwick here has quickly assessed Service's baseline performance and estimated your entitlement. We'll start, needless to say, with the overall issue of inventory. Here's what it looks like."

Zwick handed West printed sheets that read:

SERVICE DIVISION INVENTORY

	BASELINE	ENTITLEMENT
		(MILLIONS)
Raw Material	2	1.5
Work in Process	6	3
Finished Goods	4	0.5
Potential Savings		7

While West scrutinized the numbers, Moore nodded at Zwick, whose time had come to assert his empowered authority.

Zwick spoke: "As Ann says, it's faster and cheaper for Service to design and install systems right than to stockpile parts. The same goes for raw material. Once you've improved your processes, you'll be able to get by on a lot less.

"Colin, I've heard you say that there's no quality problem inside Service because the standards for your systems are absolute. That's correct as far as it goes. But the processes by which you achieve those standards can stand improvement. There's where the quality shortcoming lies. Streamlining processes will allow you to improve the quality of your customer service. You'll be more precise. You'll respond quicker and at lower cost. Take a look at your entitlement numbers and tell me what their impact might be."

Zwick passed out another printed sheet. It read:

ENTITLEMENT OBJECTIVES FOR SERVICE DIVISION

1. CUT RFQ RESPONSE TIMES BY 50%

2. CUT DELIVERY CYCLE TIMES BY 50%

3. INCREASE FIRST-PASS YIELD IN SERVICE
   MANUFACTURING TO 95%

4. REDUCE INVENTORY BY 55%

West scanned the sheet, laid it gently on the coffee table, snorted and scrutinized the ceiling. "Are you waiting for me to comment?" he said at last.

"We are," replied Moore.

"Well," said West, pressing the tips of his waxen fingers together and frowning at the ceiling, "in a word, we'd be twice as fast at getting water systems from the drawing to operation, which could mean an enormous saving to most of our customers. In our business, every week of installation time costs a couple hundred thousand dollars or more. If they could save a few weeks, clients would beat a path to our door. But...."

Here we go again, thought Moore. "The trouble is..." she prompted.

"The trouble is..." echoed Zwick, smiling.

"The trouble is," confirmed West, "that it can't be done." He went on to emphasize that, in his words, Total Cycle Time would be a "solecistic approach for Service. In a prototypical environment such as the Module Division, it can flourish, but in an idiosyncratic entity like our own, it would be an anomaly, I think."

When I grow up, thought Moore, I want to use big words just like that!

But then came the gist of West's resistance. To everyone's relief, it was expressed in ordinary English: "No offense, Zwick, but you've under-estimated how complicated it is to serve customers in a business such as ours. It is a long, intricate process: design changes, adjustments, contingencies, waiting for specifications, and, if we cut our inventories, waiting for vital equipment to be delivered. A very complex operation."

"Yep," said Zwick. "That was my impression when I did my assessment. Complicated. And that's why it *can* be done. Service is going to *un*complicate its operation and shorten its cycle times. It stands to reason that the shorter the time between a clear definition of needs and delivery, the smaller the number of things to go wrong or get revised."

Gomersall couldn't have said it better, thought Moore. And neither could I. She relaxed as Zwick continued: "If I understand you correctly, Colin, you implied that techniques which apply to manufacturing don't apply to a service business. Forget it! That was Marketing's attitude at first. People there changed their tune because they learned what we knew all along: Process barriers are generic. The same sort of barriers pop up in every type of operation. We'll eliminate those barriers. Try it, you'll like it!"

At which point Moore added, "Try it even if you don't like it. Zwick will be over to form a crossfunctional team for Service the first of the week. Okay, Zwick? Okay. Thank you, gentlemen, for your time."

As the meeting broke up, Zwick spied Gomersall in Moore's outer office thumbing through a back issue of *Modularities*. "Boy!" said Zwick as he approached his mentor, "I could've sure used you in there. I'm not used to going nose to nose with corporate VPs."

"You'll get used to it," replied Gomersall. "Ann and I agreed that I should butt out of this meeting and let you take charge. Got a minute?"

Gomersall seldom asked for a minute without planning to take at least an hour, but Zwick always said yes. The two stood by a window which, like every other, overlooked the parking lot.

"When Ann and I talked yesterday," Gomersall continued, "we also agreed that my useful time here was coming to an end. I'm a manufacturing guy; and now that the Module Division is almost at entitlement, I want to start the ball rolling at another company. Or maybe just relax."

Zwick knew what was coming next. "Wait a minute!" he broke in. "Since day one you've preached that when it comes to quality and high performance, what goes for manufacturing goes for any other operation. Seems to me you ought to stick around long enough to prove it! Meanwhile, I..."

"I have proved it. Over and over. I just haven't proved it here. This time, I want *you* to prove it. I doubt if you realize it, Zwick, but you've learned your cycle-time and quality lessons well. Here at Nodulex, you're an insider full of new, unorthodox ideas. Me, I'm stigmatized as an outsider who's overstayed his welcome, and a guy who comes from the despised manufacturing sector to boot.

"Resistant Service people are more apt to listen to you than to me, provided you know what you're talking about. You do. But you have to show the courage of your convictions day after day. Ann thinks you're up to it. So do I."

"Look, Earl, I've never run a white-collar cycle-time operation. They'll eat my lunch."

"Wrong on both counts. Your help to Jato Torres got things moving in Marketing and everyone knows it. The actions in process in Service may be harder to identify than Marketing's, but barriers are barriers." Gomersall handed a card to Zwick. "And if you get stuck, you can reach me at these numbers."

"What are your plans?"

"Before coming here I helped a plumbing fixture company near Milwaukee get itself to entitlement. I'm going to go back and make sure the new culture has been successfully internalized — you know, the Fifth I — which needs constant checking. After that, I'm gonna relax. It'll be good to sleep in my own bed and drive my own car for awhile."

"Who are you kidding, Earl? You'll be sick of that in a week!"

"Maybe, but it sounds good right now. Anyway, with so many hung-up quality programs around the country, I can stay as busy as I like. But

I'll also stay in close touch with you and Ann. I expect to return here now and then to take this company's pulse and monitor your Internalization, so you haven't seen the last of me." Gomersall looked at his heavy, expensive watch. "Ah, lunchtime. Come on, I'll buy you a cheese steak."

Although he wasn't hungry, Zwick followed Gomersall out the door. He gave himself two choices. One was to start the crossfunctional team process before Service people knew what hit them; the other was to leave town forever. Gomersall may have read his mind, for he turned to Zwick and said, "Don't sell yourself short. You know the drill and you have the authority. People will come around."

"Earl, that's *exactly* what the consultant said before he left me holding the Back On Track bag."

"That was then. This is now. The results will speak for themselves."

"The consultant told me *that*, too!"

Gomersall laughed. "Gee, Zwick, are you calling me a consultant? That's the worst thing anyone's said to me in ages! Take it back!"

"Okay, I take it back. I just hope that when you drive out of this parking lot, I feel more confident than I did back then."

"You will, I'm sure. But even if you don't, you'll still succeed because the time-based approach to quality works. Now let's eat."

Once Service had appointed its crossfunctional team, Zwick advised the participants to start at the beginning of the business process: response to customers' requests for quotations. The RFQ cycle proved to be a rat's nest of barriers. In a nutshell, the RFQ Department needed to learn how to spend less time on its estimates while improving its precision. Because customers characteristically set their own deadlines for receiving bids, the objective was not to finish estimates sooner but to start later and still meet the deadlines. Starting later, when specifications were clearer, would vastly improve the accuracy of quotations. The route to this objective was shorter cycle time.

The team found, however, that a massive cultural barrier lay athwart that goal. For years, success had been measured in terms of the size and number of RFQs in progress: The bigger the backlog, the better the performance, or so it seemed. Salespeople (Service had its own sales force) and engineers alike drew immense psychological comfort from knowing that the division was swamped with work in process. And swamped it was.

Because of such emphasis on quantity, the team found:

- Departmental people labored on several RFQs at once, which lengthened the cycle time of each

- RFQs were begun with insufficient information

- Mistakes along the way and revisions submitted by customers engendered an environment of permanent overtime and predominant fatigue

- To compensate for long delivery cycle times, RFQ people had to guesstimate which projects looked most promising so that those could be started early, before a customer commitment

- Wrong guesses about customer commitment caused many wild goose chases and a pile-up of unused finished goods.

Like all cultural barriers, the backlog fixation was so deeply entrenched that nothing short of a change in mindset was likely to dislodge it. Luckily, the remedy was straightforward. Colin West accepted the team's recommendation that the backlog measurement be abolished, substituting tested indices of merit that would force people to change their thinking patterns. Henceforward, the department's performance would be gauged by cycle time (the speed of response to RFQs), first-pass yield (in terms of the percentage of accepted bids), cost (not size) of proposals to customers, and the RFQ cycle's impact on overall job profitability.

Inside Service, RFQ had a reputation for short tempers, and for good reason. Everyone in the department was run ragged, yet no one had perceived that the permanent state of overexertion was attributable to the hefty backlog. For example, each time an RFQ stalled because of missing or insufficient information, or confusing specifications, it was put on hold and an engineer was assigned to "get the right answer." Over time, the department accumulated dozens of RFQs on hold. Every question was deferred, given an identification number, and logged into the computer system. An assigned engineer then attacked each question by telephone or correspondence. When problems crossed functional lines of expertise, as was often the case, they were sub-assigned and sub-catalogued. Large dollops of overtime were allocated to clear the most troublesome problems, but people working nights and weekends could seldom make the right customer contacts. Vast reports accumulated showing which jobs were on hold and why. Every day, a grueling meeting was held to review all delays. And then more paperwork, more meetings, more money, more delay.

In an effort to remedy this hectic situation, RFQ people had devised reams of intricate, standardized spec forms that were sent to potential clients for completion. These often did more harm than good, and they took their toll of good will. As one red-eyed engineer put it to Zwick, "This damn department is sinking under the weight of explaining why everything's out of whack!" Zwick would have said that it was sinking under the weight of its substitute process.

Zwick needed to bring Cycles of Learning to bear as soon as possible. When meeting with the divisional team, he pointed out that to all appearances the department was uninterested in learning from experience. "Instead," he ventured, "RFQ is solving the same sort of problem over and over on an à la carte basis. Each time a customer glitch surfaces — and most surface in random order — a different engineer may be assigned to the problem! Whatever know-how he or she acquires during the experience is lost. That know-how ought to be systematically examined and applied to the next problem."

Zwick instructed the team to prepare a Pareto chart analysis of the most frequently recurring departmental problems. The report revealed that the twenty most common were causing 80 percent of RFQ tie-ups. Team members were then told to develop permanent solutions that every engineer could use. When the first batch of solutions was formulized, the rest were attacked.

Feedback from Cycles of Learning began to eliminate the error-prone system. It soon became apparent that the department often failed to give customers the class of information they needed for their own decision making. It was also apparent that the department's guesstimating and internal record keeping were frequently at fault. In Total Cycle Time's terminology, first-pass yield was almost zero. As a forcing function, the team persuaded West to establish first-pass yield as a measure of each project manager's merit. Service was learning that the same generic measurements of performance applied everywhere.

No longer hostage to the big-backlog mentality, the crossfunctional team implemented a faster, more economical way of preparing quotations. The department was reorganized so that more people concentrated on fewer RFQs. That step provided new insights on the overall process. In one instance, when reviewing the problem of employee fatigue, a team member questioned the accepted method of producing engineering drawings. That challenge became an opportunity for higher quality and real cost savings.

Tradition required that Service Division engineers do all the required drawings for a given system. Because drawing requirements outnumbered engineers, this was an arduous task. Complex drawings, which required substantial engineering thought and calculations, took hours, sometimes days, to complete. Many others, however, were quite simple and could be dealt with in less than an hour.

Upon investigation, the team determined that the drawing function was woefully undisciplined. Whenever a simple drawing required attention in the queue, an experienced engineer would have to stop work on a complex drawing and dash it off. The distractions of "easy drawings," however, were quite costly. It took hours for a distracted engineer to regain his or her proper train of thought and return productively to the more complex task. A twenty-minute drawing, it was learned, cost three hours of lost time on a complex drawing. Instead of squandering engineering talent in such a manner, why not subcontract the simple ones to an outside drafting firm? The proposal was adopted. The result was a 20 to 30 percent saving in cycle time for complex drawings and a creative refocusing of Nodulex expertise.

Inside of two months, RFQ people were spending half the time they had formerly needed to complete each RFQ, which meant that the department could commence an RFQ at the last minute and still complete it on time. And by starting later, after the customer had submitted the inevitable revisions, engineers cut the distracting requests for clarification and the reworking to a minimum — a substantial payoff for customers as well as Service. Happily confronted with the RFQ improvements, West generously memoed Zwick (with a copy to Moore):

I SEE THE LIGHT. QUALITY AND PERFORMANCE WERE (AND ARE?) AN ISSUE IN SERVICE. LET'S GO TO WORK ON THE DESIGN CYCLE.

West's memo was diplomatic but behind the times. Zwick and the Service crossfunctional team had already gone to work on the design cycle.

Having learned from its RFQ experience, the team was faster at detecting hangups within the Design Department. Just as in RFQ, Design had too many engineers working on too many parts of a design, including such mundane details as drawings. Once again, talent was redeployed away from such tasks into outright engineering. As the backlog mentality receded, the number of designs, stalled and otherwise, declined.

The team then won approval to restructure the department. Various components of a job, which were formerly attacked sequentially, were now dispersed to teams that worked on them in parallel. Confronting the department's noisy, distractive atmosphere, Zwick persuaded West to divide the floor plan into large, partitioned zones without cubicles or telephones. Because Service was bringing more of its talent to bear on a smaller backlog at any one moment, cycle time fell and Cycles of Learning increased. Opportunities to improve performance on each job accelerated accordingly. The combination of stronger RFQs and quickened delivery dates were sure to increase Service's market share, for customers were assured of substantial savings.

Within a year, the hit rate on RFQs improved by almost 60 percent while the overall time to generate an RFQ was reduced by about 55 percent. Because more RFQs could now be generated, and because each was more precise, Service's market share increased.

The department with the shortest gap between baseline and entitlement was Customer Service, which supplied regularly scheduled maintenance on installed water systems and immediate assistance in the event of a client emergency. Because of the inherent characteristics of its mission, Customer Service was virtually free of inventory and able to respond at a moment's notice. Nonetheless, as the crossfunctional team demonstrated, there was room for improvement.

Why, for instance, did it take so long for the department to be reimbursed by clients? The method of billing, for one thing. Here was the procedure: A written report by a maintenance or service team leader was routed to West's office for a signoff and then mailed to the client along with an itemized bill. Altogether too much paperwork and too many non-value-added steps, said the team.

After mapping Customer Service's processes, an alternative was proposed that was beautiful in its simplicity. First, travel charges were standardized to eliminate itemizing every actual expense. That change permitted expenses to be entered on a preprinted form. Routine maintenance chores were likewise standardized and printed in a check-off format along with a form to cover the most frequent emergencies. Thus standardized, the formats served both as a report on actions taken and a bill for same. Because of their uniformity, most required no formal approval before they were submitted to a client.

Those improvements cut the cycle time of each service call; but one more process barrier had to be cleared before overall cycle time dropped as expected. This time, the problem involved habitual behavior on the part of service representatives. The newly streamlined forms proved popular; but when a service or maintenance call was finished and the appropriate form was completed, service representatives had a way of dropping it into a briefcase and heading for the next service call. The result was that days might elapse before a rep's accumulated reports were mailed in a batch to Nodulex for processing. If a call was completed at the first of a month, as much as thirty days might elapse before some report forms found their way back to accounting. And because reports bunched up at the end of each month, performance in accounting suffered accordingly. Typically, thirty more days elapsed before a bill went out to a customer.

Using the measurement of customer satisfaction, Service's maintenance and service reps were performing admirably. But when measured in terms of accounts receivable, they were prolonging cycle time at very great cost. The team determined that no less than $1.5 million in cash was tied up because of briefcase delays.

Fixing that problem and liberating that cash was also amazingly simple. Upon completing a job at a client site, the maintenance team leader would now indicate the actions taken and the appropriate charges on the forms and leave them with the client at the moment of departure. At the same time, however, a duplicate copy of the simplified bill would be faxed to West. Although the new billing format was mostly a matter of common sense, it saved the Service Division more than thirty days of billing cycle time and eliminated enough paperwork to enable the reassignment of two clerks.

West kept Moore advised of his division's march toward entitlement, and Moore, reviewing these improving prospects alone in her office, allowed herself a little momentary pleasure — just a little. Looking over the Customer Service update, she couldn't help noticing that West, by standing aside and endorsing his team's recommendations, would see his division's shrinking market share expand again and would wind up smelling like a rose. But she also couldn't help noticing an unattended barrier or two, which she planned to take up with West at a meeting three days hence.

The topic of the scheduled meeting was again inventory, Moore's perpetual flashpoint. This time, while going over Service's figures, Moore had zeroed in on the Machine Department, where inventory had come down but not enough. What was the problem?

All too aware that inventory was taboo, West nonetheless thought the amount of inventory entirely correct, and he was prepared to do a solo defense. "The answer is simple," he explained. "Twice in the late eighties, we had two contracts go haywire because one of our vendors let us down. Stretchum Incorporated supplied the elastic sheaves we use in our assemblies; they still do. We put in our order as usual only to learn that Stretchum had won a second-supplier contract with Uncle Sam that was using virtually all their capacity. As a result, Stretchum took eight months to deliver our sheaves. I vowed that would never happen again, and from then on, we've kept an eight-month supply of sheaves on hand. Doing so immunizes us against another fiasco. Now that our cycle time is falling, it is more important than ever to give customers quick response."

"Whoosh," said Moore.

"I beg your pardon?"

"Whoosh. What you hear is the sound of inventory flushing. Out it goes. We can free up another $200 thousand that way, to say nothing of the carrying charges on all those sheaves. Colin, you're talking today like an old-school manufacturing manager."

West swallowed, pressed his fingertips together, and studied the ceiling. Clearly, he was preparing a long, patient rebuttal. Moore, meanwhile, was impatiently tapping her desktop with her gold ballpoint. Slowly, her eyes also assumed a faraway cast, and she too looked toward the ceiling. Zwick, his own pencil at the ready, fought the temptation to look in the same direction.

Click! Suddenly, Moore began again, getting the drop on West. "The inventory matter is settled. But it leads directly into another of my concerns: vendor quality. Nodulex can't afford — literally can't afford — to be at the mercy of Stretchum or any other vendor. I'm embarrassed to say I didn't see this problem coming. I should have. You're right; Colin, it *is* important to respond to customers in keeping with our shortening cycle times. But to do that, we must make certain that our vendors have *their* processes under control.

"When you think of it," Moore continued, taking the dark view to which she was so often attracted, "all our cycle time improvement could be mortgaged to the slow response of vendors. Horrors! A barrier to end all barriers! Where do we go from there? I know what you're going to say, and you're right: If we flirt with new vendors, we may forfeit the good will of longtimers like Stretchum. And what if the new ones aren't up to our accelerated demands?"

Moore rose and moved to the window, taking in the parking lot below. Abruptly, she spun around, facing the seated Zwick and West. "Zwick," she said, "I want you to set up a vendor conference right here in Essington. It should happen as soon as possible, but be sure *every* vendor attends."

Zwick was writing again, fast. With Moore perched on the corner of her desk, the three quickly framed up the premise of her proposed conference. There were two objectives. One was to show suppliers how and why Service's business would improve dramatically, which should come as good news. The other, as Moore put it, was to "convince vendors that we'll drop them like hot potatoes if they don't keep pace with our cycle times."

Under the old, now unmentionable culture of Comfortability, Service had selected its vendors partly on the basis of proximity. Consequently, most were able to attend Nodulex's vendor summit without undue difficulty. So it was that after five weeks of nightmarish coordination, a senior manager from each vendor was assembled in the dining room of the

Corinthian Yacht Club for a shakedown by Ann Moore.

Addressing the group after an elegant seafood luncheon, Zwick outlined the Nodulex route to competitive quality and the positive results to date; then Moore made a seductive case for the fact that each vendor was tied to Nodulex's coattails. Nodulex, she assured everyone, would soon differentiate itself from competitors as the fastest in the business; consequently, its volume of business — and need for supplies — were certain to rise. Vendors who calibrated their schedules with Nodulex's would ride the same bandwagon. Any complaints?

Yes. Stretchum's representative stated flat out that there was no chance of accelerating his company's response to match Nodulex's. "I would be less than honest," he added, "if I didn't advise Nodulex to look for a new sheave supplier." For a moment, the finality of that statement threatened to torpedo the conference. But other, hungrier representatives wanted to explore the issue in depth. In the general discussion that followed, vendor problems were revealed to be deeper than previously imagined. The discovery, thought Moore, was like peeling an onion, including the part that brought tears to one's eyes.

A new and daunting barrier was exposed. Some vendor cycle times were dependent on others. Sannzico, for example, provided the critical imparting equipment for each Nodulex system. Like other Nodulex machines, Sannzico imparters contained special ion implants produced at nearby Gizmolab. Further discussion revealed that Gizmolab was already too slow to suit Sannzico, so the chances of the latter shortening its cycle time were not good. "How about it?" Moore asked the visiting Gizmolab representative.

"I'll take my cue from Stretchum and be frank," responded the rep. "For us, servicing Nodulex and Sannzico is a feast-or-famine proposition. Virtually no orders for months, then huge demand from each of you — simultaneously. We're too small and too busy to keep massive inventories of implants."

"And you shouldn't," replied Moore. "Exposing barriers like that one is precisely why I called this summit meeting. I want to reaffirm to all of you here the need to iron out problems collectively so that all of us work within a single, seamless business process.

"As for the three-way barrier we've just exposed, Total Cycle Time will put an end to our historically unbalanced demands on vendors. From this moment on, you should prepare to supply steady, small lots of product, but quickly. And note well: As of this meeting, Total Cycle Time has expanded beyond the four walls of Nodulex. It is now an inescapable concern for everyone in this room.

"You vendors have a lot to gain by short cycle time. And, at the risk of sounding ominous, I must add that you have no acceptable alternative. The world is changing. Expectations about quality and service are stiffening, not slackening. Thank God Nodulex took that to heart in time."

The warning unleashed several minutes of impassioned defense of the status quo, well-intentioned queries about cycle-time terminology, and even a few shrugs, which added up to general confusion. Vendors who saw the writing on the wall seemed not to have a clue as to what action was necessary.

It was now or never. Zwick proposed that Nodulex sponsor a crossvendor team. That group would identify, prioritize and eliminate barriers and non-value-added steps within the interlocked delivery cycles. "Meanwhile," he added, "you can prepare yourselves by mapping your processes and applying the Hirtle W. Zwicker Paycheck Test for Shortening Cycle Time. Whenever I'm stumped about where to begin, I ask myself what barriers I could remove if my paycheck depended on it. My paycheck *does* depend on it, so I'm always pleasantly surprised by how many barriers pop right up. With you vendors, it is a matter of determining which steps you could eliminate if your *future orders* depended on it."

"Hirtle W. Zwicker speaks the truth," added Moore. "Your future orders *do* depend on it."

Hours later, with a firm schedule for cross-vendor brainstorming in place, the meeting broke up. Moore, West, and Zwick decided to walk from the yacht club back to home base using a riverside shortcut Zwick had discovered; that way they could troubleshoot the events while they were still hot.

"Well," ventured Moore, "the good news is that Zwick is now honorary honcho of the first crossvendor team in Nodulex history, and it couldn't happen to a nicer guy."

"The bad news," added West, "is that we lost Stretchum."

"Surely there's an alternative," replied Moore.

"Correct. United Windlass is the fastest in the business with no compromise in quality. But they charge for that, and how."

"Look at it this way, Colin. By paying more to ensure quick vendor response, you'll ensure increased profitability. Remember what you told me about the impact of short cycle times. In your own words, 'clients will beat a path to our door!' Anyway, do we have a choice, strategically speaking?"

"No. As you told the vendors, our future orders depend on it."

"Well said," replied Moore. "And so succinct! Colin, I do believe you've become a convert!"

Emerging from a tree-lined pathway and approaching the company's chain-link fence, all three suddenly glimpsed the neon NO LEX CORP sign flickering on the plant's rooftop. "I know what you're thinking," Moore told the others, "and I agree. We ought to get that thing fixed. We will, we will. But I sort of like it the way it is. That sign keeps me humble. At the same time, it represents a little bit of light at the end of the tunnel. The day we're truly out of the tunnel, I'll deal with the sign, and you'll be able to read the good news on the rooftop. "Well, that's my van over there. Goodnight, gentlemen, and thanks. The end of the tunnel approaches."

It had been agreed at the summit that the crossvendor team should meet every two weeks, with informal contacts maintained as needed in between. The first meeting was held at Nodulex; each participating company would host a meeting on a revolving basis. One of the team's first findings produced a shock in Essington. Vendors unanimously pointed out that the Service Division, not they, was the major barrier to quick response.

Zwick shared this embarrassing knowledge with West and Moore during the review following the team's first session. "Here's the bottom line," he said. "Again and again, after Service puts in an order, the order gets altered, and things bog down. The guy from Askew Industries told me that it didn't pay his company to move quickly on any Nodulex order because the company always changed its mind. Better, he said, to wait until we'd finished diddling with our own specs and drawings!"

"Askew's argument is not without merit," admitted West. "We've been a bit difficult, but for a dollars-and-cents reason. After we sent our drawings to Askew, we always thought of some change that might save a percent or two of the cost. We'd change the specs accordingly."

"A percent or two?" asked Moore.

"Yes. That's nothing to be sneezed at because our profitability is so small."

"*Was* so small, you mean. In very short order, by your own admission, Service's profitability will jump. What was the effect of 'diddling with our own specs?'"

"Glad you asked, because after Zwick reported to me I did some calculations. Diddling lengthened our cycle times and postponed delivery dates, costing us several percentage points in profit."

"So to save 1 or 2 percent..."

"Don't say it, Ann. It's over. Askew and every other vendor will receive my promise to that effect. My guess is that that single breakthrough will prove worth all the trouble and effort we're expending on vendor coordination."

As they left Moore's office, West asked Zwick to accompany him to the Procurement Section loading dock. "I want you to see what I found there," he said. Zwick, who had made many trips to the loading dock, shrugged and went along. Judging from his quickened pace and tuneless whistle, West had something up his sleeve.

As they strolled toward the dock, the two chatted about recent changes in Procurement. Managed by Paul Tasca, the Procurement Section was part of the corporate financial operation, which meant that Tasca reported to Ann Moore. Shortly before Moore's arrival, and on the advice of one of the company's revolving-door consultants, the section had undergone an improvement program. Zwick recalled the program's title as a masterpiece of Jargonese: "Maximum Utilization of the Optimizer Function." In plain English, that meant getting the most out of people and resources. Tasca had taken that phrase to heart, and the results were written up in *Modularities* as an object lesson for all Nodulexers.

Back then, Procurement's inspection unit consisted of seven people, more than enough to check incoming material and route it promptly to the right department. The trouble was that the arrival of goods was unevenly spaced, so the inspectors were sometimes under-utilized or completely idle. Tasca logically reasoned that it would be more economical to have four people working full time than seven who didn't always have enough to do. Therefore, to achieve Maximum Utilization of the Optimizer Function, he reduced his inspection unit to four. In recognition of this economizing, Big Lotz had presented Tasca with a certificate which he affixed to the wall outside his cubicle for all the world to see and admire.

170

Sure enough, as he and West entered the area, Zwick spotted the certificate still hanging proudly, although Tasca was nowhere in evidence. Each of Tasca's four inspectors, though, was hard at work amidst piles of arriving material.

"Observe, if you will," said West.

"Observe what?" said Zwick.

"Everyone is very, very busy."

"Uh, Colin, that's not exactly a hanging offense at Nodulex. Are you complaining?"

"Yes. I am doing so as a one-man, ad hoc, ex-officio crossfunctional entity," said West. "Behold a barrier that is lengthening my cycle time and impeding the quality of my service to customers. Let me explain. Ever since you and Ann turned up the heat in Service, I've been beating the proverbial bushes for ways to slash our inventories, and I have implemented the team's every recommendation.

"One day, however, when I was standing right here, something jumped out at me that I'd seen a hundred times before without really noticing: the way incoming material is inspected at the dock.

"When Tasca made his celebrated improvements here, he created a barrier. Procurement may have optimized its utilizer function or whatever the gobbledygook says, but by cutting the number of inspectors, he lengthened the time of the inspection cycle. There I am in Service, against the inventory wall. Meanwhile, over here in Procurement, everything we need to maintain our shortening cycle times — pumps, custom pipes, tanks, you name it — is often stopped on the dock four weeks before these busy little bees get around to it."

"Wow," said Zwick. "It *is* a major obstruction. I'll have the team examine the situation and..."

"No. This one is mine, Zwick; on the house, so to speak. I've already looked into the matter. There's about $3 million worth of inventory languishing in Procurement. As Ann likes to point out, carrying costs on that sort of inventory may run half a million a year. All because Procurement cut its inspection team which — I checked the publicity — saved Nodulex about $50 thousand in annual wages. It would, to say the least, be economical for Tasca to add two inspectors and start measuring them on cycle time and first-pass yield instead of maximization, or optimization, or whatever the hell it is."

"Touché, Colin. Nice work. Anything else?"

"Yes. I want the pleasure of breaking the news to Ann that part of her own operation is a major barrier." West's waxy fingers fluttered in gleeful anticipation. Agreed?"

"Agreed. But I want to be there when you tell her!"

West's discovery was an exception that proved the rule about operations under Moore's direct command. In general, Moore had practiced what she preached to her divisions. Having learned the ropes during her Briktek years, she had lost little time before recycling her know-how to her direct reports inside Nodulex. At Briktek, Moore heard every justification in the book for poor white-collar productivity. The most obnoxious of these, she thought, was denial of the connection between overcomplicated procedures and substandard quality. And the nerve center of overcomplicated procedures at Nodulex was the Management Systems Department, whose computerized capability fed the corporate appetite for data, measurements, and reports.

During his last on-site conference with Moore, Gomersall had advised the CEO to "use Management Systems as a teaching example of how to shake out some solid quality and productivity gains." Although he liked to call himself a manufacturing type, Gomersall knew better than anyone that many more bodies were buried in white-collar sectors. "There's a good reason to start with Management Systems. Computerization has done a lot to improve this company: in payroll, closing the books, reporting to the IRS, keeping track of stockholders' status, employee benefits, that sort of thing. I can remember what monumental effort all that required back in the Stone Age before computers."

Moore knew where Gomersall was heading. She had heard him lecture on the subject at Stanford, so she broke in: "Those improvements lowered the cost of doing business and fostered the mindset that computer mechanization is generally cost-effective."

"Right," said Gomersall, smiling. "And that thinking has created a monster in company after company. Once management decided that computer systems could generate savings, the temptation to add more and more information services became irresistible. It just seemed right. Nobody asked how much would be saved in real dollars. Soon, systems had become chaotic. Then, to impart order to the chaos, controls and safeguards were added. Up went the cost of new systems and the time necessary to create them."

"You could be talking about Nodulex," said Moore. "The fit is perfect. Know what I found when I arrived? Managers all over the company who had no mandate to document or back up their systems were asking for PCs and justifying them as a cost-cutting measure!"

"It's crazy," agreed Gomersall. "I once visited an electronics company whose main computer generated a prodigious number of reports. I calculated that at average reading speed, the entire staff of that company would need a week to get through one day's worth of information produced by that computer."

"It is not that bad at Nodulex," replied Moore, "but it's close. For once, though, timing is on our side. When Big Lotz quit as CEO, his systems manager left for greener pastures. I've replaced her with an eager beaver who, I'm sure, will be amenable to some radical restructuring. I'll keep you informed about our progress."

Shortly after Gomersall's departure, Moore met with with her new systems manager. Because he possessed advanced degrees in mathematics and computer science, Alvon Cheatham seemed more boy genius than eager beaver. With sleepy eyelids and a hangdog moustache, Cheatham was a ringer for the comedian Richard Pryor; but there the similarity ended. He walked with short shuffling steps, his unswinging arms at the vertical, and he habitually looked at the floor. His unvarying uniform was dark trousers, a striped dress shirt without a tie, and what was possibly the last existing pair of ripple-sole shoes in the Quaker City. Cheatham's pockets bulged with assorted sour balls to which he was addicted.

Palming a cellophane candy wrapper when he entered Moore's office, he stuffed the wrapper into his shirt pocket, shook hands, clicked his ballpoint and sat down with a pad on his lap.

"Ah," said Moore, "that's what I like: a man ready to get down to business. Well, hold on to your hat, Alvon. You're about to lead a change that will make a vital difference throughout the Nodulex. Your Systems group is going to help the entire company become more productive. As people become more effective, they'll be smarter about what to ask of you; and, as a result, Management Systems will operate at a higher quality level." Now comes the defensive reply, she thought.

Cheatham did not disappoint her: "Systems already gives all departments all the information they want. We're here to serve those needs, and we help wherever we can. No one can accuse us of being unresponsive or, um, uncooperative. And you probably know that all our major projects are approved by the Management Systems Committee."

Moore knew about the Management Systems Committee. Its members included Cheatham, Howie Lotz, Colin West, Jato Torres, and lately, at her insistence, Hirtle Zwicker. "I don't doubt that you get top-level approval, and I'm certainly not implying that Systems is unresponsive. But — talk to me honestly as a newcomer, Alvon — are you comfortable with the value-added content of the information you provide?"

Cheatham clucked the sourball he had hidden in his cheek. If Moore was looking for a nerve, she had hit it. "Ours is not to reason why," Cheatham said. "At least that's the view of the Systems Committee. My guess is that even though the committee is made up of, umm, top dogs, they don't always understand what they're approving. Speaking for myself, I'd say that some of the requests we get are pretty esoteric. The number of requests keeps increasing, and no one ever discontinues a request. But my specialty is providing services, not critiquing them, so we keep cranking 'em out."

"Understood. But it sounds as if a lot of expensive and ponderous information is moving around the company without any meaningful clarification of its value. So, with your cooperation, I'm going to change that." On cue, Cheatham's ballpoint clicked again.

"Henceforth," Moore continued, "all current systems, new and old, will be reexamined regardless of Systems Committee approval. Furthermore, *they will have to justify themselves according to their quantifiable value to the company.* Say, for example, a computer-based quality system promises to improve the product line by 4 percent. In that case, the manufacturing and quality budgets of the user will be reduced accordingly. After all, improved quality always reduces cost. Inasmuch as improved quality permits us to make and inspect 4 percent less than before, there should be a corresponding reduction in manufacturing cost, right? Every new system must improve the efficiency of the company on a measurable basis."

A huge smile illuminated Cheatham's normally droopy countenance. "I love it," he said, chuckling.

Aha, thought Moore, another kindred spirit. What a time saver that's going to be. "Can you spare one of those sourballs?" she asked. "Thanks." Continuing as Cheatham jotted notes, she said, "I want you to determine the monthly cost of the systems you offer so that the user is paying only for what he or she uses, the way a motorist pays only for the gas he or she pumps. Establish a pump price for CPU time, a pump price for disk storage, a pump price for printing, and so on. *No more allocations.*" Cheatham was now gleefully rocking back and forth as he wrote.

"Now," said Moore, "when the Systems equipment has been rationally priced, have one of your software geniuses devise a way for the last page of every computer report to print a cost summary of resources used. In the case of a screen, make it the last screen of data. We'll also want to include the journal voucher number that identifies where the charges will go."

"Discipline is the name of this game" said Cheatham.

"Discipline *is* the name of this game," Moore agreed. "And in the interest of improving this game, I'm enacting a corporate law that anyone who discontinues a report will receive an immediate, one-for-one credit on his or her expense budget. In the case of multiple users, after a dropout occurs, those continuing to use a report will share the increased cost equally.

"Finally, the prices for computer resources will be revalued and approved only once a year. Of course, with advances in hardware and software, I would expect costs to go down."

Cheatham's eyes closed in thought. Absent mindedly, he pulled from his pocket two orange sourballs, proffering one to Moore, who was still working on her first. He unwrapped the other as he spoke. "Let me say that, umm, I think the accountability approach is great, and I see what you meant about making Systems more productive. Financial accountability will make people look more carefully at their requests. When they start dropping the ones they can live without — and there are a dozens of those, I'll bet — my people can improve the quality of our services."

"Exactly. A lighter load will give you the opportunity to streamline your own organization."

"But there's one angle that worries me."

"What's that?"

"People will dump their systems like the plague, stop working through our main computer, and switch to PCs."

"Not with the kind of accountability I'll enforce. PCs are resource eaters for big data-based systems, and they become obsolete before they're paid for. The cost per track on a billion-byte disk has got to be less than the space per track on any PC. The same goes for CPU speeds and data transfer. But there may be a few instances when a PC is preferable to a mainframe. In such cases, I would expect you to help users make the right decision. Develop a matrix that can spread throughout the organization. Tell people when a calculator is a better solution than a Cray, or when a networked central computer is worse than a real-time PC at measuring temperatures every three seconds."

Working together, Moore and Cheatham agreed that every user of the computer systems already in place within Nodulex should be polled:

- What does this report cost you per year?

- Within the time span of each copy of this report, what decisions do you make for the company that are equal or more cost-effective than the cost of the report?

- Is there any logic you must apply to the information you receive, or is it usable as is?

- If you apply logic to received information, can the task be accomplished by the main computer? If not, why not?

- If you have not already done so above, please quantify the value of the information you receive. Based on your analysis of value added, do you wish to continue this report?

"I dunno," said Cheatham, looking over the just-completed list. "We may be creating a monster here. We'll be inundated with cancellations and requests to change existing reports."

"That's the idea!" replied Moore. "Remember, all systems have to be quantified, and the costs will have to be ponied up in people and expense budgets. Look on the bright side, Alvon. Your people will end up working on systems that really do something for the company. We both know you've got your work cut out for you. But Nodulex will be a better, more responsive organization because of it. Now here's the difficult part: I want these policies and procedures in effect *ten working days from now*."

"Gee, Ann, you don't ask for much."

"And I'm not through asking. When the dust settles, you can expect to undertake a similar program for the telecommunications side of your operation. I'm not just picking on the Management Systems function. Every function in a company must understand that it exists to make the

176

company more responsive in quality, cost, and cycle time. Every function must develop a rational charge scheme so the people they serve can evaluate its worth. And to remain effectively streamlined, every function must utilize regularly the understanding of the people it serves. I think I'll have those points printed up and posted throughout the corporate staff areas."

Cheatham rose and extended his hand with a smile. "I knew there was a good reason to take this job," he said. "I just didn't know how good that reason was. I think I'll title my first memo to users 'THE END OF VOODOO SYSTEMS APPROVAL!'"

"Catchy but a little antagonistic. Try 'SYSTEMS OWNERS WILL BE RESPONSIBLE FOR SYSTEMS RESULTS.'" That approach makes it a motherhood issue. Now get going, stay in touch, and start thinking about how to improve the quality of our telecommunications."

Two weeks later, when Cheatham's new program was up and running, Moore wished Gomersall were around to share the auspicious news. In addition to the quality payoff, estimates indicated that Nodulex would be many thousands of dollars richer each month thanks to the improvements in the management systems function.

Although far from the scene, Gomersall had kept in close touch with Zwick by faxed or mailed memos. This time it was Zwick's turn; he wanted to outline the progress made in the Service Division and gloat a little. He knew of course that neither the progress nor the gloating would surprise Gomersall. Zwick kept his fax short: After eight months of effort, the Service Division was 70 percent of the way toward its entitlement goals. As for the original estimate, Zwick could see that, if anything, he had been too conservative.

Gomersall must have been right beside his fax machine because, less than a minute after Zwick had finished his transmission, the phone rang.

"Zwick? It is Earl in Chicago. Yep, I've finished pulsing the plumbing fixture company; they're fine. But listen. I've gotten some serious nibbles from a few companies in Philly, and I wondered if you had something to do with it. An outfit called Sannzico wants to take the cycle-time route à la Nodulex — a formal program. So does something called Gizmolab. Yesterday, I got a plaintive call from Stretchum Incorporated. They're *really* in a hurry! Any of these ring a bell with you?"

"Sit down, Earl," answered Zwick. "This could take a while!"

COMMENTARY

Chapter Seven

Quality Performance in Service Businesses

By the time Nodulex turned its attention to the Service Division, its new, time-based culture was producing results and gathering momentum. Perhaps that was why Service VP Colin West was able to accept the concept that manufacturing-based performance improvement techniques apply to any type of business. As a consequence, his division enjoyed a relatively smooth transition to competitive quality. Would that it were that easy elsewhere, especially in service-based companies where there is no understanding of manufacturing realities.

Easy or not, the truth is that the fundamental methods of detecting and removing barriers are generic and therefore will work in any enterprise. Controlling the number of actions in process is likewise a necessary goal for any business that cares about competitive quality. And the most important quality measurement is first-pass yield. Anywhere. Everywhere.

Implementation within the Nodulex Service Division was by no means unusual. Nor were the conditions that cried out for reform and uniformity. Nor were the results. The Projects Department operated under performance measurements meaningful only to itself and Corporate Accounting. The Quotation Department, where merit was defined by the number of actions in process, was drowning in uncompleted tasks, overtime, substitute processes, delays, and meetings to examine the reason for delays, all of which were rationalized as the cost of doing business.

Those symptomatic distractions were in fact the cost of unnecessarily long cycle times. First-pass yield was unheard of. Cycles of Learning were few and far between, and no feedback loop existed to trap the lessons of experience. The mere sight of so many overworked engineers going off in different directions without a single Cycle of Learning was probably enough to give a man like Earl Gomersall nightmares. Yet it happens all the time.

Any service business that undertakes a time-based quality effort can expect that:

- Quality and competitiveness will improve as processes are simplified and Cycles of Learning take effect

- The same generic cultural performance barriers that plague manufacturing-based businesses constitute root-cause barriers in white-collar sectors

- Management will be exposed to goal setting of a far more aggressive nature than in the past

- Quaint concepts such as using contractual front money for "negotiating inventory" or measuring performance by accounting conveniences will be scrapped in favor of meaningful, enforceable alternatives

- Entrenched substitute processes may be more numerous than in manufacturing-based environments

- Many substitute processes have been generated in the interest of "improved customer service"

- Continuous improvement will require timely interfacing with vendors and willingness to modify processes to accommodate vendor needs

- It may be necessary to actually assist a vendor in simplifying processes, shortening cycle time, and raising first-pass yield

- Overall white-collar productivity can improve dramatically: between 25 percent and *300* percent.

The Shape of Things to Come

The Information phase of the Five I's should make clear to all hands that reaching entitlement does not provide a summit from which a company can complacently look down on its struggling competitors. Entitlement is a major milestone but is necessarily momentary. Every competitive company must convince its people that continuous improvement — Life After Entitlement — is essential. With Total Cycle Time driving performance and quality, a company now has the know-how and mindset to exploit options that were once completely out of reach (and are probably still out of the competition's reach).

What is the best way to leverage existing competitive quality? Where should additional resources be deployed? Could strategic alliances with customers transcend traditional relationships? These are the sort of questions that Ann Moore and her seasoned team members were about to face.

Chapter Eight

Beyond Entitlement

Six months later, when he heard that he was to arrange another bash at the Corinthian Yacht Club, Zwick's first impulse was to pass the buck. "I'm having déjà vu," he told Moore as they faced each other above the scowling gull on the CEO's office coffee table. "Before you arrived, when I was Czar of the Back On Track program, my first chore was to throw a kickoff party at the Yacht Club."

Moore laughed. "I know," she said. "I trust the party was more successful than the program."

"Couldn't resist that, could you? Well, the party *was* great and it stirred up enthusiasm just as hoped. What's the reason for a party this time?"

"I think everyone deserves some celebration and congratulation for the job they did getting to entitlement. But that's not all. A party will help internalize the new culture by marking the end of the old culture — a milestone, if you will. It shouldn't be too reminiscent of Back On Track because, psychologically speaking, I want people to start living in the future. A year from now, when they remember the good time they had, they should see that it was the beginning of something."

Back On Track's happy beginning and unceremonious end had made Zwick wary of corporate fiestas. And with the limited time and resources at his disposal, this new one could not be much different from the old one. Different chow, perhaps; but the site would be the same. So would the band, which was an institution at every Nodulex event. God forbid that the weather should be different.

As always, however, he threw himself into the assignment Moore had given him. He asked VPs Lotz, West, and Torres to devise lists of divisional heroes who would receive public recognition at the party. For a decorative motif, Zwick had the leftover BACK ON TRACK! banner that still hung forlornly above the main manufacturing line relettered DON'T LOOK BACK! (Waste not, want, not!) He also commandeered a dozen fifty-five gallon oil drums which he had painted red, white, and blue, and set them aside.

The night before the scheduled party, Moore took the principals in the Nodulex turnaround out to celebrate. The outing, Moore's idea, constituted official recognition that Modules, Service, and Marketing had all made it to entitlement. The Zwickers, Lotzes, Wests, and Jato Torres (who came stag) convened at a fashionably late hour at a newly opened Szechwan restaurant on Chestnut Street in Center City, where Moore had reserved a private alcove.

Walking through the restaurant's main dining room gave Zwick the creeps. He had gobbled his way through literally dozens of Chinese eateries in the U.S. and Canada, but never had he beheld such pretentious splendor. Not a single Oriental was to be seen at the tables, which he took as an ominous sign. The furnishings were a cunning, Occidental symphony of mirrors and metallic art deco, and the help were in formal livery. Yuppie Heaven, he thought. Good thing the boss is picking up the tab. The boss and the other guests seemed right at home, so he decided to relax and have fun. Which he did, although he was firmly diverted to a spot two chairs down from Moore by Torres, who seemed determined to sit next to the CEO.

The delicacies were safely bland, not "★ ★ ★ — HOT AND SPICY!" as promised on the oversize menus, but everything was tasty and attractively prepared. Sandra Lotz and Nancy West, seasoned corporate wives, made cheerful chit-chat only when spoken to, leaving the limelight to the VIPs. After a cautionary, under-the-table kick from her husband, the more voluble Becky Zwicker did likewise.

Over a dessert of lychees in Grand Marnier, Becky and Zwick witnessed for the first time a tabletop ceremony dear to the hearts of senior executives: the distribution of joke awards. Moore had several of these gifts, which she withdrew with a flourish from a Wanamaker's shopping bag at her side.

Lotz, the first recipient, cautiously unwrapped a silver-papered gift box. Inside was a bronzed polystyrene cup, a survivor of the original cup game, mounted on a walnut base inscribed LITTLE LOTZ WORKS BEST. This prompted nervous chuckles. No one had ever called the VP Little Lotz to his face. "Forgive the ungrammatical pun, Howie," said Moore. "It is just a play on the lot-size lesson — and a token of my admiration for your willingness to try almost anything new in manufacturing."

"I knew my nickname would come into its own someday," said Lotz, genuinely pleased. Everyone relaxed again.

"Here's yours," said Moore to West, who quickly unwrapped a thick volume. It was a thesaurus fitted with a handwritten dustcover reading "SERVICE DIVISION CODEBREAKER." Moore explained: "Whenever you're tempted to circulate something in writing," she said, "consult this handy guide. It'll provide you with ordinary synonyms for the five-dollar words you like to shower on us. Think of the time we'll all save!"

Julie West emphatically seconded the sentiment, and her husband looked quite happy with his unexpected gift. "Words fail," he said, probably for the first time in his life.

"We doubt it." said Zwick. "But if that's the case, let me, umm, reiterate that availing yourself of the etymological alternatives within this tome will optimize the opportunity to produce interoffice communications that are irrefutably paradigmatic. And I mean that in the transactional sense, of course."

"Okay! Okay!" said West as soon as the laughter and applause subsided, "But you can't teach an old dog new tricks, so perhaps everyone should keep copies of this book for translation purposes. No? In that case, I'll treasure it always. I may even use it. Thanks. It is... How should I put this simply? It's nice to be one of the boys. In this case, 'boys' is a generic term."

Zwick was hoping that as a non-VP, he might evade the gift trap. No dice. Moore passed him a festive package big enough to hold a vacuum cleaner. He tore open one end and peered in. "Gee thanks," he said. "What no home should be without. And just in time for dessert!" Zwick shook the box and about a dozen scarlet, made-in-Hong-Kong, plastic lobsters plopped onto the table. "Everybody take a few. There's at least a hundred more in this box!"

"They're to comfort you next summer if you're too busy to get away to Nova Scotia," explained Moore. Zwick and Becky exchanged alarmed glances. "Hey, Zwickers, I'm just kidding!" Moore added in the nick of time. Everyone at the table scooped up a plastic crustacean as a keepsake.

"That concludes our little ceremony," said Moore, signaling for the check. "Glad you all could make it tonight. We've got a big day tomorrow."

At the checkroom near the door, West turned suddenly to Torres, saying, "Jato, you didn't get a gift."

"What can you give the man who has everything?" quipped Moore.

"Not quite everything, but I'm trying," replied Torres, shooting his monogrammed cuffs as the group emerged onto Chestnut Street. "Anyhow, things are going so well in Marketing that I gave myself a gift. Nothing ostentatious mind you: a Lexus Coupe. Black."

"Glad you didn't go away emptyhanded," said Zwick. After handshakes all around, the couples headed for a parking garage around the corner, leaving Torres and Moore alone on the street.

"Here's my cab," said Moore. "Nice of you to come tonight, Jato." Torres held the door for her as she entered the taxi. "Believe it or not," she said once inside, "I've got a few loose ends to tie up at the office before tomorrow's celebration."

"Umm, Ann, I wonder if you'd be free for another dinner in, say, a week?"

"Business or pleasure?"

"Well, I..."

"Sure. Call me Tuesday. Driver, I need to get to Essington. Nodulex Corporation."

"You got it lady," said the driver. "NO LEX CORP coming right up!"

Twenty minutes later, with her mind on tomorrow's details, Moore flicked on the lights of her office and saw instantly that something was different. The little gull she kept on her coffee table had been moved to her desktop. Good heavens! On her coffee table perched the Mother Of All Gulls, a handcarved, black-and-white, webfooted giant squatting on bright yellow legs as thick as broomsticks. Unlike the antique it had replaced, this critter had a fresh, spanking new look. And it was *smiling*. Love at first sight.

Running her hand over the mysterious sculpture, Moore spotted a tag looped around one leg. It read

> For obvious reasons, this bird was too big
> to present to you at dinner. But one good deed
> deserves another, so I hope you'll give her a good
> home.

184

While vacationing in Nova Scotia last
Christmas courtesy of Nodulex, I spied her
on a woodcarver's fence in Cheticamp. She was
intended to decorate a seafood joint, but as soon
as I saw her I knew she was meant to be Nodulex's
quality mascot. Earl agrees. Hope you do too.
Thanks, Ann.
Zwick

The weather cooperated with the scheduled corporate party, which turned out to be, in Moore's words, quite a blast. This time, a company holiday had been declared, so all shifts were on hand for a truly massive indoor-outdoor barbecue.

Following the formalities, just before the crowd began to dissipate, came the hit of the entire day: a ceremony that had cost Zwick a week of red tape and permits. As the Essington Stompers blew a fanfare, a hose truck filled with off-duty firemen bounced noisily onto the scene. The red, white, and blue oil drums Zwick had set aside were rolled to the lawn just below the bandstand and a fire was started in each.

Once the flames were roaring, a Nodulex delivery van backed up to the bandstand. Its insides bulged with paper: computer print-outs, files, charts, reports of all kinds — an enormous, leaden pile. Heaving himself up and inside the cargo well, Zwick nudged the top of the pile, and it began to slide like syrup from the truck onto the ground. Moore grabbed an armful and, on cue, so did Lotz, Torres, and West. Moore mounted the platform and held up an unfolding strip of computer paper that threatened to entwine her as she stepped to a microphone.

"This stuff," she said, "is a small part of the paper burden borne by Nodulex under the old measurements, pointless checkups, and galloping information systems. Look at it: file after file, drawer after drawer, report after report. None of it added a nickel's worth of value. Today we say goodbye to it all. For good, right?"

"RIGHT!" the crowd shouted in agreement. Then, as the Essington Stompers struck up "Happy Days Are Here Again." Moore trotted to the edge of the platform and slam-dunked the first armful of paper into a blazing drum. In a flash, people got the message. A few, then many, ran to the van, scooping up armloads of paper and pitching them into the flames. Everyone cheered and the visiting firemen clanged their truck's bell.

Three bonfires gulped paper for at least a half an hour, after which the thirsty crowd returned to the beer stand. Nothing like it had ever been seen at the Corinthian Yacht Club.

The festivities ended at dark. "What a day!" said Zwick as he, Moore, and the VPs strolled along the shortcut back to the Nodulex parking lot. "The fires even kept the mosquitoes away. People caught the new culture, and it'll stay with them."

"It'll stay with them as long as we uphold it," replied Moore as the group cleared the trees and passed through the chain-link fence. "But there was one other symbol of the Old Regime that had to go. Behold," she said, pointing to the roof of the plant.

"I'll be damned!" exclaimed West as the group looked up.

"Gee, that feels even better than it looks." affirmed the astounded Zwick. High atop the flat roof the unbroken words NODULEX CORPORATION beamed down from the company sign.

So why don't I feel on top of the world? Moore wondered a few minutes later, alone in her darkened office. The rosy glow of the newly-repaired sign outside permeated the silent room, causing the carved gull's huge wingspread to cast a spooky, batlike shadow on one wall. Moore had to ask herself that question after every professional and personal triumph, and the answer was always the same: Things, good as they were, could be better.

Ambushed by the insecure perfectionism that had dogged her since childhood, she suddenly remembered a painful scene several years earlier when, just before the door closed behind him forever, departing Spouse No. 2 had fired a final salvo: "Ann, you should learn the lesson of The Olde Philosopher: In life, you gotta concentrate on the doughnut, not the hole."

To which Moore had had the last marital word for the last time: "Anyone who follows The Olde Philosopher will end up with little doughnuts and big holes. Better you than me."

Slam!

But tonight of all nights should be different, shouldn't it? By any standard, Nodulex's attainment of Total Cycle Time was a very big doughnut indeed. There was no catch. Couldn't she for once simply relax, bask in the sign's ruddy glow and enjoy some peace of mind?

No. It was not within her to relax no matter how rosy the glow. Besides, she rationalized, it was her responsibility at Nodulex never to relax or be blindsided by change or self-delusion. The world hadn't stood still during the company's tortuous struggle to entitlement. Now that Nodulex had arrived, it needed to leverage its unique strengths and devise new strategies unavailable to the baseline competition. Failure to do so would invite competitor catch-up and forfeit Nodulex's substantial edge.

What new strategies?

Even after close to two years as CEO, Moore still felt keenly her lack of expertise in modules and systems. She had better get her Business Improvement Team focused without delay.

Hanging on for dear life in the passenger seat of Zwick's new red Miata, flinching nervously at the rain-swept traffic streaked along I-95, Howie Lotz marveled at how different the world looked when someone else did the driving. Different and a helluva lot more dangerous. Lotz himself drove the interstate daily, but always at rush hour in the tanklike sanctuary of his Mercedes. Today's mid-afternoon traffic was light, probably out of respect for the teeming thunderstorm.

Lotz and Zwick were returning to Nodulex from a crossvendor meeting in Bristol, and Lotz couldn't wait for the trip to end. Thrilled with his new toy, Zwick whipped the roadster in and out of the passing lane, maneuvering around slower, more prudent drivers. On his face was the assured determination of a fighter ace.

With each lurch and surge, Lotz's grip tightened on the dashboard and he fought down his need to protest. Zwick was a nice guy, and he had become something of a buddy for the last few months, so Lotz measured the value of his own life against the risk of offending his pal. Life came out second. He resolved to play it cool and concentrate on counting the spherical, white refinery tanks whizzing past.

"Yow!" In an instant, Lotz's view changed to a closeup of a gigantic blue fender that was immediately obscured by an enveloping sheet of water. As the wave washed over the Miata, Lotz felt the car snap left and accelerate sharply. Just behind, like the clappers of doom, came the blast of a diesel horn.

"Oops, Sorry!" said Zwick, snorting sheepishly. "That semi must've been in my blind spot. I better take it slower, huh? You can let go of the dashboard now, Howie."

Lotz relaxed a little. "I'm not uptight because of your driving," he lied, choosing friendship over truth. "I'm a control freak. I get jumpy whenever anyone but me is at the wheel. Also, I'm on a short fuse today, courtesy of Ann Moore."

"The future catastrophe scenario, right?"

"Right. What is it with her? A catastrophe should be the last thing on her mind. I mean, all divisions are operating at entitlement. We're killing our competitors. Briktek loves us. The board is ecstatic. We've been the subject of a CNN business feature. And *she* starts prophesying disaster. Did you have a hand in writing that scenario?"

"Guilty as charged. Ann outlined it and I took it from there."

"If you ask me, Zwick, you took it too far. My people hit the ceiling when they read it. They've busted their butts to get competitive, so handing them that alarming forecast was, well, insulting!" Lotz pulled from the papers on his lap a much-annotated, Xeroxed document. "Look at this," he said, pointing to page three. "No! Look at the road; I'll read it to you. Ah, here it is: 'If Nodulex continues to perform at its entitlement, profits can be expected to drop from 25 to 5 percent. Meanwhile, determined competitors, having reached entitled levels of quality and performance, will have recaptured lost market share and will compete successfully against Nodulex in both Modules and Service.' That forecast sounds like the pickle we were in *before* entitlement. A helluva note. Maybe we should have spared ourselves the trouble."

"Easy does it, Howie. It's not a forecast. It's a worst-case scenario. Those things could happen — make that *will* happen — if Nodulex sits on its collective duff after entitlement. Some of our competitors will get their acts together and try to do what we've done. A few might even succeed. Modulanswer announced last week that it's starting a radical time-management program; and remember, Modulanswer's quality and response time are already good. First us, then Modulanswer; there might be a chain reaction and there's nothing we can do about it." Although he did not say so, Lotz knew a great deal about Modulanswer's catch-up plan. It was real. Zwick continued: "That being the case, Ann says we can expect profits to drop by a point or two within a year if we stay put at entitlement. Nodulex's relative position and market share will continue to move south unless we continue beyond our present quality and performance levels.

"That worst-case scenario is part of Ann's program of Internalization. It reminds everyone that entitlement is a moving objective. We can't just stop and rest on our oars. That would invite backsliding and reversion to old habits. If your Module people think the push is over, they still have some serious internalizing to do. Maybe the disaster scenario is just what the doctor ordered."

"Wrong. It is Ann 'Fly-in-the-Ointment' Moore who should see the doctor. The scenario isn't realistic because, obviously, we aren't gonna rest on our oars. We now have resources we can deploy to improve our performance even more. We also have a built-in ability to trap knowledge. In other words, we can't help but improve."

"Granted," said Zwick as the Miata bounced across the puddly Nodulex parking lot. "But it's a jungle out there. If we get complacent, or backslide, or if our competitors are as smart as they look, the disaster scenario might not be far off the mark. So what do we do about all this? Well, for starters, the Business Improvement Team can identify ways and means of keeping our competitive lead. Or, to use Ann's phrase, 'the weapons that will kill the competition.' Another thing...."

"What's that?"

"Right now, for a short while, Nodulex has a golden window of opportunity to identify new markets or new products — areas open only to us because of Total Cycle Time — and move in those strategic directions. That'll be the agenda at the BIT's next meeting. Well, here we are."

"Zwick, it's been a real adventure riding with you. The least I can do in return is drive us both in my car next time. See you at the BIT meeting — if you're still in one piece. Happy landings."

The evening before the BIT meeting, reflecting privately upon the disaster scenario, Moore had to admit that she had once again succumbed to her hardwired jitters. She and Zwick had overdone the gloom and doom. All the same, the report's pessimism should provoke some creative thinking about strategic alternatives.

Sticking to her guns the next day, she made no excuses for the disaster scenario. But getting BIT members to think strategically was tough going. The division VPs, who had lately gorged on praise, were testy and off balance. At first, everybody wanted to sharpshoot the premise of a gloomy future. Colin West, for example: "Ann, I take issue with your fear of declining market share. The Service Division's market share has never been higher, and it's increasing by the month."

Moore was ready for this. "True, Colin, and well done. But your market share is growing faster than the market you serve. Obviously, there will be diminishing returns from growing fast in a slow-growing market."

"Which reminds me," put in Lotz, "of the Minidule. The plant's qual-

189

ity and cycle time turnaround caused our market share on that item to surge. Then, when Modulanswer dropped its version altogether, we had the market to ourselves. It was fun while it lasted, but demand is drying up because the device is just too complicated. As a result, we've got 100 percent of a market that's more trouble than it's worth."

"That's a good example of why we need a major strategic thrust," said Moore. "A thrust that will *recharacterize* these businesses." She paused. Look at their faces, she thought. I know what they're thinking: Bosslady has found a new buzzword. Well, they're right. She pressed on. "Recharacterization will insure us against the kind of disaster outlined in my worst-case scenario.

"Nodulex must identify and aggressively pursue several strategic pathways. It goes without saying that we will improve continuously because that's built into our processes. Such being the case, our first step is to determine what benefits our customers might gain from our new quality and responsiveness.

"Our next step will be to get our customers involved. Our precision and quick response can be worth a fortune to a customer. In Service, for example, every day we save in the installation of a water system saves a client almost $200 thousand."

"Speaking of which," said West, "we got a water system on line at Canadian Semiconductor last month in half the usual time, saving CS at least a couple of million. Needless to say, the CEO was ecstatic. He told me personally that if we could cut installation cycle time by another 20 percent, customer savings would be so big that no client could afford to hire anyone but us. We'd be in a class all by ourselves. We intend to reach that 20 percent solution."

On came The Headlight. Moore followed up: "We've got the attention of clients like CS because of our existing capability. Meanwhile, we should get potential clients thinking about what advantages they'll enjoy as our response gets even quicker, and what they might do, strategically thinking, with all the money we'll save them.

"The same thing applies to Modules. What new opportunities exist for Briktek now that we've simplified and shortened Briktek's task? Neater designs? New Briktek products brought to market faster? More consumer applications for Briktek products? The fulfillment of Briktek's wildest dreams, whatever they are? Let's ask them. Briktek's answers to those questions have strategic value for us.

"Another approach of course is to widen the existing module and service markets by going beyond North America. Jato, I'm sure you saw that coming."

"Sure did. I only wish we'd moved in that direction sooner."

"Well, until lately, we weren't in a position to strategize creatively. Things are radically, *radically* different this time around. Now that we're profitable and responsive to customers, we can use our Cycles of Learning database to select and invest in state-of-the-art technology. To date, nobody else has that capability.

"New resources will steepen and accelerate the continuous improvement we've come to expect using Total Cycle Time. That will afford us enough capacity to serve new markets and serve them well. Accordingly, our second strategic thrust will be to demonstrate new uses for modules to potential customers. After we've brainstormed about this, I'll organize a small committee on applications.

"Which brings me to the most exciting part, recharacterization, by which we can virtually recast the future. Let's discard the Nodulex/entitlement paradigm. Let's strategize above and beyond Minidules and water systems. New departures."

"You mean entirely new lines of products?" asked Lotz.

"Sure. And to that end, I'm going to add more design/development talent to the BIT. But for the rest of today's meeting, I want to brainstorm about what present quality features we could leverage. Howie?"

"That's easy. The Module Division has learned to match close tolerance cores and barrels better than anyone else in the country — maybe the world."

"And our environment-resistant coatings are tops, period," added manufacturing manager Rick Jacobs. "There isn't a competitor around that even comes close to our coating formula."

Lotz again: "We have a crosstrained work force with a true quality orientation that can move product through the plant like the wind. Oh, and we can manage inventories better than anyone else."

"All of which are features that can easily be marketed," said Torres.

"In that case," said Moore, "I propose that all future Module Division products be designed and developed around those distinctive quality features, in close consultation with Marketing. We should also deliberately design our future around the other competencies we developed under Total Cycle Time: order entry, accounts receivable, vendor relations, and so on.

"Now keeping all this in mind, let's brainstorm. Zwick?"

Zwick strode to an easel supporting a flip-chart tablet and began to write down the ideas that came forth. They and their verbal justifications were surprisingly varied. As later prioritized and assigned to various BIT members, they were as follows:

- Develop an exotic new line of modules made of the most durable (and costly) materials available. Virtually all module manufacturers avoid this market opportunity because of the inventory investment costs. But with Nodulex's low cycle time and just-in-time delivery capability, such products can be delivered and billed almost before payments for raw material come due (Howie Lotz/Rick Jacobs).

- In Service, offer architects and contractors the option of waiting to order water systems until other details of a building project are clarified. Nodulex will still deliver on time, and the reduced number of engineering changes will constitute a substantial saving (Colin West).

- Search out new product niches where close-tolerance quality is crucial (Rick Jacobs/Jay Torres).

- Instigate an immediate customer wish-list survey in which clients would "design" new modules to enhance their finished product offerings (Ann Moore/Hirtle Zwicker).

- Market the Module Division's environmental coating to non-module industries. Competitive analysis will soon reveal the secret to module competitors, but by then, Nodulex will have a dominant share of the coating business (Jay Torres).

- Create a financial matrix for customers that will reliably demonstrate how much inventory money and carrying costs they can save by utilizing Nodulex's quick-response capability (Alvon Cheatham).

- Offer order entry and billing services to companies lacking short-cycle-time precision (Hirtle Zwicker; later discarded as too complicated and too far removed from the strategic focus).

"Okay," said Moore after the suggestions had petered out. "Some of these ideas are great, some not so great; but that's what brainstorming is all about. These will get us started. The next step is for you to time-line and budget the ideas assigned to you. Next meeting, we'll fine-tune and develop action plans.

"Remember, gentlemen, these approaches, which orient on our present strengths, constitute just one thrust of an overall five-year success plan. The others will require a lot more strategic imagination. We meet again in three weeks."

The BIT brainstormers had made a solid start, but as the day wore on, Moore was again dogged by general anxiety that somehow the turnaround at Nodulex was in jeopardy and that her attempts to leverage its present strengths would not suffice to secure the company. She was especially worried about competitor catch-up. True, for the immediate future, Nodulex would have competitors on the defensive, chewing their nails about their own survival. Some would certainly fall by the wayside. But the others? Modulanswer's current quality and response were far better than that of Nodulex at the time of her arrival. Could that company leapfrog over Nodulex with its own time-based quality program? Was strategic thinking possibly sharper there than here? If Nodulex was to leverage its present superiority and widen its lead on competitors, there was no time to lose. Same old story! Everything at the company had changed but that.

At home in her study, having finished a microwaved Budget Gourmet dinner and a tossed salad, she put a Billie Holiday tape on the stereo and ran through the day's brainstorming list one more time. All the ideas now seemed parochial, too involved with the company's current infrastructure and mindset. The list was a case of creative leveraging but it wasn't even close to the recharacterization she had been looking for. Her uneasiness expanded. The last time she had felt this anxious was the day she called Earl Gomersall from a phone booth somewhere in Lebanon County.

Click!

Moore killed the stereo and punched the second auto-dial button on her telephone.

"Gomersall here."

No preliminaries. "Moore here. We're trying to shape a strategic thrust and it's not up to snuff. No real inspiration. Wait — I'm faxing you our list of product strategies right now."

193

As the BIT list rolled through Moore's fax machine, Gomersall asked, "Are you sure your worries aren't exaggerated? You know you're hard to please and never satisfied.... Wait while I scan your fax." No sound at the other end for about a minute; then Gomersall spoke again. "Well, it's a pretty creative inside list."

"*Inside* list? Are you damning with faint praise, Earl?"

"Yeah. I can see that your team has internalized short-cycle-time culture and plans accordingly. The ideas are good as far as they go but they don't add up to a future breakthrough."

"They don't really recharacterize the company, right?" put in Moore.

Gomersall snorted. "That's a good term; where'd you get it? Right. When it comes to real vision, your BIT people are limited because they're too close to the problem. Even you."

"How about selling us some outside perspective, then?" asked Moore. "I'm not looking for a lot of help, but I'd like an insurance policy against a major strategic oversight. I'll pay accordingly."

"You won't have to pay much because my scheduled quarterly visits to Nodulex will dovetail with your strategic thrust once you get it properly focused. For instance, I can provide you with technological updates and software recommendations to further refine your processes. You'll get a lot of bang for your bucks now that you're operating at entitlement. That's an important edge because your competitors are still throwing resources at symptomatic problems.

"Advice like that is effective at the process level. But you're really asking for guidance at the systems level and beyond. I can offer objectivity at that altitude because, thank God, I can walk away from the company and take a long, hard look. When we first talked, you had that sort of perspective; but you're an insider now. Outside perspective may make the difference between process-driven improvement and real strategic thrust."

"Despite the jargon, that's the best insurance pitch I've heard in years, or at least since we first talked," said Moore. "Now I can sleep tonight."

"Ann, you do overdramatize, and I think you like it. Look, I'm due to visit Nodulex in three weeks to take the company's pulse. Schedule a BIT meeting for then and, if it's okay, I'll sit in."

"It's okay," said Moore, who really did sleep well that night.

It wasn't quite okay with other BIT members, however, when upon convening they beheld the guest in their midst. Lotz's greeting, "Back from the grave, Earl?" said it all. Even after Moore explained that Gomersall was aboard to impart outside objectivity to the BIT's strategizing, people remained cool.

"Can't blame them, Ann," said Gomersall in a whispered aside. "I'm like a doctor who treated them when they were ill. Now that they're well, I'm an unpleasant reminder of bad days. Happens at every company."

The group began its strategy session by extending the ideas it had brainstormed a few weeks earlier. Lotz and West had done their homework. "I want to address the need for broader thinking in the make/market cycle," said Lotz. "We ought to review our packaging. Right now, our module quality is the highest in history. Those devices are shipped to customers in the safest, most protective package there is. But maybe that's not enough. The quality of our customer service would go up if our packaging were further refined. Customers would be better served by a package designed for easiest possible use in their process. Their cycle time would drop demonstrably when using our packaged modules, and their quality would rise because our better package assured proper installation. We could also adapt our packaging to automatic equipment. It's worth noting that such improvements would forge a customized bond between us and our clients." Heads nodded in approval.

"By an uncanny coincidence, Howie's idea is similar to my own," said West, chuckling. "In Service, our cycle time could be even shorter if we packaged our equipment here on a tailor-made basis to our construction order. At present, we almost always have to repalletize material at the site. Prestaging at Nodulex would greatly ease organizational pressure at a client's site. It's worth exploring."

"It sure is," said Gomersall addressing the group for the first time. "But having reached entitlement, I think you need to develop strategies that go beyond..."

"We understand that," said Lotz, whose impatience was never far below the surface. "We're already under orders to, umm, what's that word again, Ann? Recaricature?"

"*Recharacterize.*"

"Yeah. Recharacterize. Easier said than done, apparently."

The strategy session had suddenly grounded. In a painful silence that lasted about a minute but seemed like ten, West studied the conference room ceiling. Lotz pressed his fingers into his temples and pored over a tablet bearing scrawled notes. Torres scrutinized his perfectly manicured fingernails. Moore jumpily clicked the tip of her gold ballpoint in and out.

Gomersall seemed to be scratching at a dot on his tie with a fingernail.

"Well, nobody said it would be easy," said Moore at last.

Lotz tried again. "Maybe we can't see the strategic woods for the trees, Earl. How about jump-starting us with your celebrated outsider wisdom?"

That was the invitation Gomersall had waited for. "Okay," he began. "Nodulex has module manufacturing down to a science. You've optimized the process as it stands and can refine it further through Cycles of Learning and new resources. But I wonder if there might be a better way to accomplish the same function through different products."

"Are you talking about devices that might do what modules can do, only better?" asked Jacobs.

"Yeah. I'm not suggesting that the company's whole R&D effort be spent on this question. Your first strategic responsibility is to protect the basic business. But keep in mind how, in electronics, vacuum tubes reached a state of extreme refinement only to be blown away by the transistor. By the same token, Nodulex would be crazy not to explore alternative devices. Suppose some other company introduces a device that renders modules obsolete? Or, looking on the bright side, suppose Nodulex introduces such a device? Good-bye Modulanswer."

"Good-bye Modulanswer. I like the sound of that," said Moore.

"Anything else?" said Lotz, edgy again.

"Well, there's always Stretchum," muttered Gomersall, rolling his unsmoked cigar from one side of his mouth to the other. All hands turned to him, awaiting further explanation.

"Stretchum," he repeated.

"As in those-bastards-who-dropped-us-like-a-hot-potato-the-minute-we-told-them-to-match-our-cycle-times?" replied Lotz. "I never saw a vendor so independent. They were too busy with government contracting to bother with us!"

"And then what?" asked Gomersall.

"We switched to another sheave vendor," said West. "Had to. United Windlass had the will and the skill we needed. But it was a headache making that switch, and it cost us. It *still* costs us: about 10 percent of our total material bill, which is 2 percent more than Stretchum did even with their frequent delays and quality screw-ups."

"Did it cost Stretchum?"

"Funny you should ask that, Earl," Lotz replied. "I read the other day in a trade magazine — *Module Age*, I think — that now that the Cold War has evaporated, Stretchum is on hard times. Their military business has been slashed and, of course, they're too slow for commercial houses like us. How times change, and it couldn't happen to a nicer bunch of guys! Yeah, I'd say parting with us did cost Stretchum."

For some time, Moore had been watching this exchange intently. Abruptly, she leaned forward and asked Gomersall why he had brought up Stretchum.

"Because," replied Gomersall, "in its own way, Stretchum is also at a strategic crossroads. Looked at from Nodulex's angle, it's a company whose poor quality was affordable until it became too big for its britches, so good riddance. Looked at from an outsider's perspective..."

Click! Moore completed the sentence, punctuating it with repeated jabs at the tabletop with her pen: "Stretchum is a company caught by long cycle times, losing market share hand over fist and possibly doomed. If Stretchum had Total Cycle Time, that wouldn't have happened. More important, if *we* applied Total Cycle Time to Stretchum, we could get out a superior product at far lower cost than anyone else in the business."

Gomersall and Moore were clearly on the same wave length and, after a jolt of understanding jerked him out of his drooping posture, so was Lotz: "If Stretchum and Nodulex both had Total Cycle Time, it would mean a saving for us of 4 percent, the equivalent of millions in new sales! And it would open up all sorts of opportunities for better designs. It might even open a door for us to defense contracting."

"Hold it," said Zwick. "Are we talking about *acquiring* Stretchum?"

"I guess we are," Moore confirmed. "With the cash we now have on hand, I think we could manage an outright purchase. Talk about deploying resources...." She tossed her pen on the table and sank back into her chair.

"Call it recharacterizing," said Lotz with a cackle. "Or for Stretchum, call it poetic justice. And as long as we're on a roll, why don't we just acquire Briktek?"

"All in good time, Howie," said Moore, peering over the tops of her half-lenses and rewarding Lotz with The Headlight. "All in good time."

Some months later, Moore met with Gomersall in Chicago. "The weeks since the BIT meeting you attended have been more surprising and interesting than I could have imagined," she told him. "It is almost as if our strategizing stirred up some sort of psychic energy."

Moore was between planes at O'Hare, so Gomersall had driven over to spend an hour with her in the Crown Room Club. The two sat in adjoining high-backed chairs over mineral water (Moore) and a Manhattan on the rocks (Gomersall). A chic, fragrant hostess had just handed Moore her boarding passes. Moore halted her conversation a moment and took a sip, allowing Gomersall's eyes to follow the retreating steps of the hostess.

"As I was saying..."

"Oh, sorry Ann. I was listening, honest. Surprising in what way? Make a story out of it so I'll get the full effect."

"Well, as the Olde Philosopher once said, the universe works in mysterious ways. Two days after you left Nodulex, I had another anxiety attack. Suppose the Stretchum strategy was too expensive? Suppose our top dogs left Nodulex and we had to bring in people untrained in time-based quality? That sort of thing."

"So what else is new?"

"Granted. But I was particularly edgy that day. I'd agreed to attend a benefit preview of the Philadelphia Antiques Show which, in case you don't know, is a highlight of the city's social season. Lots of industry biggies were bound to be present, and I wanted to be at my best."

"And were you?"

"Not at first. I always attend such functions alone, and I find them a bit pretentious, even intimidating. After a couple of cocktails, I decided to have a good time, so I wandered about, taking in a spectacular array of art and antiques, all of it for sale."

"Buy anything for your collection?"

"Zilch. Unaffordable. But I made a game out of it. The exhibitors pretended their stuff wasn't too pricey, and I pretended that money was no object. Anyway, I was letting one of those smoothies try to sell me a whirligig, when who should appear at my side but Briktek's design director, Arthur Baldwin. Have you heard of him? No? Well, during my Briktek years, he was one of the fair-haired boys, and deservedly so, because he really had vision when it came to new product concepts. It turns out that we're both folk art collectors, which I never knew before. He's also very attractive in a Joe-College way, even though he fancies himself a ladies' man and tries to prove it at every turn. In fact, since then I've... but that's another story.

"Picture it: In the midst of this dressy, blue-chip extravaganza, Artie sidles up to me with a real look of anticipation in his eye. 'What a delightful coincidence, meeting you here,' he says. Before I can retaliate with small talk, he launches into a business spiel about a 'whole new era for Briktek and a chance of the century for Nodulex.' Now, that was a line I'd never heard before, even from Artie. I told him the century was about over and that Nodulex was in very good shape, thank you.

"'That's just the point!' he said. 'We want to engage Nodulex as a major supplier of micromechanicals for our new line.' I could see he was on the level. For the next twenty minutes, the two of us stood in the middle of a crowded aisle at the show, blocking some serious upscale transactions and talking about micromechanicals.

"The gist of the talk was that Briktek is developing a major strategic thrust, the manufacture of microminiaturized motors and servos. All kinds of applications: medical, consumer, military, you name it. Artie will be in charge. In view of the Nodulex turnaround — and the fact that the two companies speak the same cultural language — Artie wants to involve us in that strategy from the ground up."

Gomersall had finished his drink and was crunching ice cubes between his teeth as he spoke: "What was your response?"

"My first thought, I must admit, was how nice it would be to work with Artie. The second, I'm ashamed to say, was to admit that I know almost nothing about micromechanicals, which is the truth. Artie just laughed. 'You didn't know anything about Brikbats or Minidules either,' he said. Then and there, it clicked in my mind that micromechanicals would recharacterize Nodulex and complete our strategic thrust. And it took an outsider to come up with it. Suddenly, I was very, very glad I'd come to the show!

"That was on a Friday night. I couldn't sleep for the whole weekend. First thing Monday, I took the BIT to Briktek to hear the whole pitch. They sold us."

"Wait a minute. You're going for Stretchum, right? And you have your board's approval for an outright purchase. No pun intended, but isn't it a bit of a stretch to..."

"Micromechanicals will require an infusion of outside cash. The BIT's plan is to create a brand-new, autonomous organization based on Total Cycle Time. We're going to treat that venture as a disciplined high-tech startup and we hope to interest venture capitalists in the prospect. As an alternative, we might locate a fledgling company with the requisite know-how, buy it, and install the right culture. Any direction you might give us along those lines will be greatly appreciated."

"Let me do some thinking. Suppose you do sell the board on this strategy...?"

"I can."

"Whose going to be in charge?"

"You can probably guess. Howie Lotz. He wants it so bad he can taste it. Between you and me, Howie has been playing footsie with Modulanswer ever since his division made entitlement. Even though he has ambivalent feelings about his family's business and would like to prove himself outside Nodulex, I think he suffers from a Little Lotz complex. Howie, remember, is not yet a member of the Nodulex board, although that's a mistake I plan to rectify. Nodulex can't afford to lose him and Big Lotz knows it. A seat on the board and the presidency of an autonomous startup would be a neat solution. Rick Jacobs can replace Howie as Module VP."

"And Stretchum?"

"Managing Stretchum is mainly a job of imparting Total Cycle Time quality into an established business."

"Zwick?"

"Zwick. He's ready. Or he will be after some intensive senior management training. Stretchum is local, which means Zwick won't even have to move; although with the jump his salary will take he may want to."

"Does he know about this?"

"Nope. When the acquisition plan was okayed, I hoped he would ask for the job. He didn't, so I plan to nudge him when I get back to the City of Brotherly Love. Quality is now integral to our processes, so it is a matter of months before we formally disband the quality crew. They're being retrained even as I speak."

"Zwick will be flabbergasted. Do you think he'll take it? Maybe you're overestimating his ambition."

"I'm surprised at you, Earl. Maybe you're underestimating my powers of persuasion."

"Maybe I am. At least I don't underestimate your powers of leadership. When you telephoned me from the boondocks two years ago, you struck me as someone in turmoil about the responsibility you'd accepted. When we met face to face, I could see that you had the requisite professional equipment and enjoyed moderate acceptance from your subordinates. *Enjoyed* is the wrong word in your case, because you were your own harshest critic."

"That, in a nutshell, is the story of my life."

"Is it still the story of your life?" Gomersall asked. His gaze moved to his hands, which were fiddling with a tabletop ashtray. Personal talk did not come easy to him.

"Could be," answered Moore. "But it's under control. When I first called you, I was momentarily buffaloed by my lack of know-how in modules and water systems. I kept asking myself, 'What's a nice girl like you doing in a place like this?' I do some of my best thinking when I'm buffaloed, but for awhile, it seemed as though I had walked the plank, career-wise."

"Is that feeling a thing of the past?"

"Mostly. If it isn't I'll handle it, same as always. In any case, it won't impact Stretchum, or micros, or whatever."

"I haven't the slightest doubt about that."

Gomersall's comment brought out the high-beam. "I appreciate you saying that. It's good to have a second opinion."

"A second, *outside* opinion."

"Precisely. And thanks. For everything."

"Advice is cheap. You did all the work. Of course, your work is just beginning! It'll be fun to watch."

From the corner of her eye, Moore caught sight of the foxy hostess gesturing toward her and pointing to a wall-mounted clock. "Uh-oh," she exclaimed, "it's later than we thought. Gotta hustle!" Gomersall snatched up his unopened briefcase and helped Moore assemble her carry-on luggage.

Emerging from the hushed clubroom onto the noisy terminal concourse, the two broke into a trot, then a run. Even in high heels, Moore pulled ahead. "One last thing," said Gomersall, puffing slightly. "When Zwick begins to shape up Stretchum, tell him not to call the turnaround Back On Track!"

"Right!" Without looking back, Moore saluted with her boarding pass and disappeared into the dark portal of a flight gate.

With the dinner trays removed and various passengers compulsively lining up to use the lavatories, the 727 was still more than an hour out of Philadelphia International, which gave Moore time to practice relaxing. She had never been good at working during a commercial flight but she was even worse at making small talk with fellow passengers. A snooze was out of the question.

She closed her eyes to give them a moment's rest. Immediately and inevitably, a cavalcade of strategic ideas and decisions began to resound and ricochet inside her head. It was an altogether different batch of concerns than those which had seemed so daunting only two years back. Bigger, too. Hindsight now made that original anxiety seem almost quaint.

That was then; what about now? Earl's personal reassurance meant something. Times had changed and Nodulex was a whole new ballgame. She was probably equal to the challenge, but Earl had hit the nail on the head when he remarked that she was her own harshest taskmaster. Anxiety was always a problem; but when it came to challenge, it was not in her to refuse. And, as she now knew, the flip side of her anxiety was an insatiable curiosity about where all this would go.

Was she game? Of course. But there were still times when she saw herself as the Kid from Briktek. Would she ever reach a plateau of satisfaction, or peace of mind, or at least comfort? Certainly not. With effort she might manage to balance her professional persona with her private self, whatever that was. Time for an overhaul in that department! Time to deal with the fact that her private life was too private, too isolated. Solitude had had its uses; but what, now, was the point of it?

She was abruptly jarred by the touch of a flight attendant who asked that she raise her seatback for landing. A look at her watch told her she had been asleep for almost an hour.

It was another hour before she disarmed the security system and stepped through the front door of her silent townhouse. The throw of a switch bathed her living room in a warm glow and spotlighted the friendly faces of her collection. Although force of habit impelled her to check all her telephone messages, she decided to test herself: no more interruptions until tomorrow. She was tired and wanted to be at her best when she sprung the Stretchum surprise on Zwick the next morning. She made for the stairs, then turned around. It was no use, she had to know what was on the answering machine.

One message: "Ann, this is Zwick. I want to see you about the Stretchum acquisition. I've been doing some thinking. I know it'll floor you, but I think I'm the one to manage that operation. Can we talk?"